1966

S o n s
o f
S c i e n c e

SONS

OF

SCIENCE

---

*The Story of the Smithsonian Institution
and its Leaders*

PAUL H. OEHSER

Henry Schuman · New York

This Book Is

Dedicated to the Memory

of

JAMES SMITHSON

"My name shall live," he said, "my name shall live
In the memory of man when vain titles
Are forgotten.   But who am I to boast?
You ask me my name.   Well, I will tell you . . .

"My father was the most high, puissant,
And noble prince Hugh Percy (born Hugh Smithson),
The Earl and first Duke of Northumberland,
Earl Percy, Baron Warkworth and Lovaine,
Lord Lieutenant and Custos Rotulorum
Of Middlesex and Northumberland Counties
And of all America, and a Lord
Of His Majesty's most Honorable
And Privy Council and Knight of the most
Noble Order of the Garter, et cetera—
One of the handsomest men in all England.
And my mother?   Elizabeth Keate Macie,
The heiress of the Hungerfords of Studley,
A widow, and descended from a King . . .
The best blood of England flows in my veins,
Yet this avails me not.   But who am I?
I am James Lewis Macie, or James Smithson,
A commoner, born in France out of wedlock,
Master of Arts from Pembroke College, Oxford,
Fellow of the Royal Society.

"Yes, once I thrilled at the great name of Percy:
Like Sidney, two hundred years ago now,

'I never heard the ancient song of Percy
And Douglas that I found not my heart moved
More than with a trumpet.'   Save for a marriage
I'd be a Percy too.   I've felt it keen,
But think me not bitter about it now—
That was long ago.   Now I'm getting on:
I am sixty-one and must think of death;
I am lonely and ill; there's not much left
For me—two, or three, or four years, perhaps . . .

"No ignorance is without loss to man,
No error without evil, and therefore
I have loved truth and have dabbled in science;
That has been my pleasure, and it may be
(Who knows?) I have enlarged those lurid specks
In the vast field of darkness.   But also
I have loved fame, that 'last infirmity
Of noble mind.'   'Fame is the spur,' said Milton.
Now by this earth's wealth which has come to me
I vow to make it true as I have dreamed:
The name of Smithson shall be linked with truth
And with the spread of knowledge through the world,
For ignorance has been my enemy
As it is all mankind's."

              So having said,
With deliberate speech and firm countenance,
He took up his pen and began to write
These bare words:

          "I, James Smithson, son to Hugh
And Elizabeth . . . this twenty-third day
Of October, year eighteen twenty-six,
Do make this my last will and testament . . .
And I bequeath . . . to the United States
Of America all my property
To found at Washington an Institution . . ."

So was his duty done, his dream reborn.
"I shall not altogether die," he said;
"Smithson shall live when Percys are extinct,
Until the world at last shall know the truth
And be forever free."

CONTENTS

PLATE 29. Instruments developed at the Astrophysical Observatory for solar studies. The two lower instruments are silver-disk pyrheliometers for measuring total solar radiation; the upper one is a pyranometer for measuring the brightness of known area of sky around the sun

PLATE 28. Charles Greeley Abbot, fifth secretary of the
Smithsonian Institution, 1928-1944

PLATE 26. The Natural History Building, completed in 1909, housing three departments of the National Museum and the National Collection of Fine Arts

PLATE 27. The Hall of Vertebrate Paleontology,
United States National Museum

PLATE 25. Dr. Walcott and party at his fossil quarry on the southwest slope of Mount Wapta, nine miles north of Field, British Columbia

all of the Smithsonian's great, he will be very wrong, for in a hundred years its roster has included scores of outstanding scientists whose names can be little more than mentioned in this brief account. They are those faithful servants who work behind the scenes and are the lifeblood of any organization. And they are not forgotten.

Acknowledgments

MANY PERSONS have helped in the writing of this book. For reading parts of the manuscript and offering valuable suggestions I want to thank especially Dr. Charles G. Abbot, Dr. Alexander Wetmore, John E. Graf, Dr. John L. Keddy, Dr. R. S. Bassler, Laurence Vail Coleman, Paul E. Garber, and Miss Rose A. Palmer. Miss Gladys O. Visel assisted in assembling the chronology of Smithsonian history at the end. I am indebted, too, to Mrs. Phyllis W. Prescott for her expert typing of the manuscript. Dr. Frank L. Campbell, former editor of the *Scientific Monthly,* has allowed me to reprint from that magazine my poem on James Smithson as a dedication, and the Jewish Publication Society of America, Philadelphia, has kindly given permission to quote from Dr. Cyrus Adler's autobiography, *I Have Considered the Days.* The chapter on Joseph Henry appeared first in the *Journal of the Washington Academy of Sciences* and part of that on George Brown Goode in the *Scientific Monthly.* "Interlude" is revised from an essay first published in the *Washington Post* under the title "Footnote to Science." The verses on page 109 were first printed in *Science* as a tribute to Dr. Leonhard Stejneger on his ninetieth birthday. Unless otherwise indicated, the photographs for the illustrations have been furnished through the courtesy of the Smithsonian Institution. The Institution also has generously allowed me access to certain unpublished material in its possession bearing on Smithsonian history.

New Jersey (now Princeton University), was elected the first secretary to head the new organization.

Henry was a noted scientist; any doubt concerning the scientific nature of the course which the Smithsonian would pursue was thus dispelled by his election. He saw clearly the work before him and proposed that the Institution should begin by supporting scientific research, both through projects of its own (then small) staff and through grants to outside workers in important fields of investigation. To diffuse knowledge he planned that the Institution should publish the results of original research for distribution throughout the world (*per orbem*, says the Smithsonian seal). By these means, Henry believed, the spirit of Smithson's expressed intent could best be followed, and the general plan and principles that he laid down formed the basis for the structure on which the Smithsonian was built. Even today, research (both through field exploration and laboratory investigation) and publication are the core of its activities. It has tried to maintain this course, all the while excluding no branch of knowledge from its rightful province. Its specialization in certain fields has been due partly to the policy of the Institution not to engage in activities adequately provided for by other organizations, and partly to the particular interests of those who have guided its work.

All the secretaries of the Smithsonian have been scientists. Secretary Henry, at his death in 1878, was succeeded by Spencer Fullerton Baird, biologist; Baird in 1887 by Samuel Pierpont Langley, physicist and astronomer; Langley in 1907 by Charles Doolittle Walcott, geologist; Walcott in 1928 by Charles Greeley Abbot, astrophysicist; and Abbot in 1945 by Alexander Wetmore, biologist.

It will be seen at once that this book is not an exhaustive chronological history of the Smithsonian. Rather, the spotlight has been turned upon the six or eight men who have been most influential in guiding the Institution's course and who, besides, have been eminent scientists in their own right. But if the reader supposes that these are

The Freer Gallery of Art
The National Gallery of Art (under its separate
    Board of Trustees)
The National Air Museum
The Canal Zone Biological Area

Through the years, then, the Smithsonian has attained
a unique position: it enjoys the advantages of a privately
endowed institution and at the same time is an establishment of the United States Government. The funds derived from the income of Smithson's bequest and from
other gifts that have been added from time to time are
used as a private endowment, with the United States
Treasury conveniently acting as the Smithsonian's bank.
At the same time, it must have the support of the United
States Government, because of diverse administrative and
other duties that Congress has placed upon the Institution: preserving the nation's treasures (its museums and
art galleries), studying the cultures of native American
peoples (Bureau of American Ethnology), maintaining a
national zoo, facilitating the exchange of scientific publications throughout the world (International Exchange
Service), and carrying on fundamental research of national importance (Astrophysical Observatory); accordingly it enjoys all the privileges that this status confers.

Because James Smithson was a scientist himself, it is
natural that those who determined the direction the Institution was to take should have steered it into scientific
channels. Even so, much heated debate occurred in Congress before it finally passed the bill that formally and
legally established the Institution. At almost every session
of Congress for more than a decade proposals and counter-
proposals were introduced or considered. Not until August 10, 1846, could President Polk sign the bill and the
busy legislators on Capitol Hill resume their concern with
such matters as the Wilmot Proviso, the Oregon question,
and a war with Mexico. On December 3, 1846, Prof.
Joseph Henry, 49-year-old physicist from the College of

at Washington an institution for the increase and diffusion of knowledge among men." That, in more or less abstract words, is the essence of what the Smithsonian is. Yet when the visitor comes to Washington he sees an old, red-stone, cathedral-like building that is called the Smithsonian. He sees two large museum buildings and a hangar-like aircraft structure and is told that these are part of the Smithsonian. He visits the magnificent National Gallery of Art nearby and the Freer Art Gallery and is told that these, too, belong with the Smithsonian. He goes out to the Zoo in Rock Creek Park and learns that this National Zoological Park is under Smithsonian direction. It all becomes a bit confusing.

The explanation lies in the interpretation that has through the century been placed on James Smithson's words as contained in his will. After all, "increase and diffusion of knowledge among men" is a pretty large order and would seem to indicate that Smithson's intention was not to limit in any way the scope or direction of the knowledge to be disseminated. When the Institution was founded in 1846 it operated as a single unit under the funds provided in the original bequest. Gradually, however, Congress found it necessary to underwrite some of the projects that began under the aegis of the Institution: the income from $500,000 simply could not stretch far enough. Later, it seemed convenient to utilize the Smithsonian organization and prestige to administer newly created Government agencies, so that today, in addition to the Smithsonian Institution proper, ten "bureaus," partly or wholly supported by Congressional appropriations, make up the Smithsonian family:

> The United States National Museum
> The International Exchange Service
> The Astrophysical Observatory
> The National Collection of Fine Arts
> The Bureau of American Ethnology
> The National Zoological Park

INTRODUCTION

What Is the Smithsonian Institution?

THE SMITHSONIAN INSTITUTION began as the nebulous dream of a man seeking to perpetuate his name and at the same time to serve the human race. Faced, at the age of sixty-one, with the problem of disposing of his fortune of about £100,000, James Smithson, a bachelor Englishman, drew up a will that made history in the field of science. The Institution that grew from his dream is now more than a hundred years old—its centenary was celebrated in 1946. As it goes into its second century it seems fitting to retell its story, with special attention given to the men who have shaped its destiny and have helped to make it one of the world's leading cultural and scientific centers.

I have heard people ask—people who all their lives have known the name Smithsonian—just what is the Smithsonian Institution? Paradoxically, the answer is simple, yet it is not simple. For the basic answer we must go back to James Smithson's will. He wanted, he said, "to found

ILLUSTRATIONS

PLATE 1.   James Smithson, founder of the Smithsonian Institution.
From a miniature by Johns, 1816

PLATE 2.   James Smithson as an Oxford student, 1786 (Artist unknown)

Sons
of
Science

1

JAMES SMITHSON AND
HIS WILL

THE STORY of the Smithsonian Institution must
start with the lonely man who gave it birth. This
story begins in England in the mid-eighteenth century, in the year 1765 when James Smithson was born.[1]

Background and Early Years

NO SPECIAL SIGNIFICANCE attaches to the year. England was
enjoying a brief period of peace, but George III had succeeded to the throne, and dissatisfaction rumbled across
the water from the American colonies. Peace was to be
short-lived. Indeed, James Smithson was to see little peace
during his entire lifetime. Before his death in 1829 he
would live through Britain's two wars with America, the
French Revolution, the war with Napoleon, and several

[1] Smithson, according to investigations of Langley and Adler, was born
in France but was brought to England for his education and naturalized.

lesser international embroglios. The affairs of Europe then, as now, were in almost constant turmoil.

But so, too, was Smithson's own life in a turmoil, and it is in his personal disappointments that we find some indication of the reason for his unique benefaction. First of all, he was an illegitimate child, a circumstance that might have had less important consequences for him had his father not been of the nobility. But his father was no less a person than the first Duke of Northumberland[2] (born Hugh Smithson). The Smithsons were an old family remotely related to the Percys, and the Duke by Act of Parliament took the name Percy. Sir Hugh was rich and handsome. Throughout his life, if we are to credit an obituary notice in the *Gentleman's Magazine,* "he sustained his exalted rank with the greatest dignity, generosity, and splendor, and will ever be considered as one of the first characters of that age of which he constituted so distinguished an ornament. . . . His Grace's extensive charities to the poor, his constant encouragement of literature and the polite arts, and his generous patronage of every kind of merit, make his death truly a public loss." He was buried in Westminster Abbey, with these words inscribed on his coffin-plate:

The most high puissant & most noble Prince
Hugh Percy, Duke & Earle of Northumberland
Earl Percy, Baron Warkworth & Lovaine & Bar[t]
Lord Lieutenant & Custos Rotulorum of the
Counties of Middlesex & Northumberland, of
the City & Liberty of Westminster & of the
Town & County of the Town of Newcastle
upon Tyne, Vice Admiral of the County of
Northumberland & of all America, one of
the Lords of his Majesty's most Hon[ble]
Privy Council, & Knight of the most noble
Order of the Garter.
Died on the 6th Day of June, 1786,
In the 74th Year of his Age.

2 He was made Duke of Northumberland in 1766, the year after James Smithson was born.

2

Rightful lineage to the House of Percy, the inheritance of titles and wealth, and all that nobility conveyed were something for an English boy to cherish. The name of Percy was one for an impressionable youth just out of college to conjure with. It was a name deep-rooted in English and Scottish history, legend, and literature. Had not Sir Philip Sidney, 200 years before, exclaimed, "I never heard the old song of *Percy* and *Douglas* [i.e., "The Ancient Ballad of Chevy-Chase"], that I found not my heart moved more than with a Trumpet"? To be cheated out of all this by the accident of birth was justifiable cause for rancor.

From his mother James Smithson's family heritage was scarcely less distinguished. She was Elizabeth Hungerford Keate Macie and at the time of James's birth the widow of James Macie, a country gentleman of Bath. She was heiress of the Hungerfords of Studley, and lineally descended from Henry VII through Charles, Duke of Somerset, her great-granduncle, and was cousin of Hugh Smithson's wife Elizabeth Percy. Little more is known of Elizabeth Macie except that she inherited the property of the Hungerfords of Studley in 1766. It was probably from his mother that James Smithson in turn received a considerable part of his fortune.

So, on two counts, Smithson was of noble birth. In later years he wrote in one of his manuscripts: "The best blood of England flows in my veins; on my father's side I am a Northumberland, on my mother's I am related to Kings, but this avails me not. My name shall live in the memory of man when the titles of the Northumberlands and the Percys are extinct and forgotten." We can only guess how deeply he resented the loss of his birthright, but just as deep was his determination to obliterate the bar sinister and forever perpetuate the name Smithson.

Scientific Development

WHEN HE WAS SEVENTEEN, in 1782, Smithson entered Pembroke College, Oxford, and was registered under the name James Lewis Macie. It appears that he continued to use his mother's name for several years, and it is not known exactly when he applied to the Crown for permission to take the name Smithson. Little is recorded of his life at Oxford. We do know, however, that his studies there soon began to develop his latent scientific inclinations, which afterward were to afford him so much satisfaction.

The immediate motives that led Smithson to follow the life of a scientist are only conjectural, but it may be that the infectious spirit of the age was largely responsible. The close of the eighteenth century was a period of discovery. It was the day of Priestley, Volta, Ritter, Kant, Lamarck, Goethe, Cuvier, Herschel, Davy, Watt, and scores of other brilliant and productive minds; and it would be only natural for a young man of Smithson's intellectual bent to be infected with the enthusiasms of the times, especially inasmuch as some of his friends were similarly inclined toward science. Samuel P. Langley in his memoir on Smithson refers to a surviving tradition that "he was the best chemist and mineralogist of his year" and says that it was at Oxford that "he appears to have already conceived that devotion to scientific research which characterized all his future life."

When only nineteen, and while still at Pembroke, he took a vacation geological tour through New Castle, Edinburgh, Glasgow, Dumbarton, Tarbet, Inverary, Oban, Arran, and the island of Staffa, in company with the Italian Count Andrioni and M. Faujas de St. Fond, "the celebrated geologist of France." His journal account of this expedition shows him to have been a young enthusiast and, for one so young, singularly diligent in recording the minutiae of his scientific observations of ores and minerals. He was apparently such an extraordinary student that he attracted considerable attention, especially for his proficiency in chemistry. The Duke of Northumberland's investment in his son's education was not expended on a wastrel. James was graduated from Pembroke

4

College on May 26, 1786, with the degree of Master of Arts.

His precocity as a man of science must have earned him a prodigious reputation, for only eleven months after his graduation he was elected a Fellow of the Royal Society of London. This was indeed a distinction, conferred only on recognized merit of the highest order. Membership in this ancient Society had been the ambition of the elite of English "philosophers" ever since its inception in 1662. It had been founded by such men as the Honourable Robert Boyle, Sir Christopher Wren, and Dr. John Wilkins, and it numbered among its first members the great Isaac Newton. In the American colonies, before their own scientific societies had begun to spring up, the Royal Society claimed among its membership John Winthrop, William Penn, William Byrd II, Cotton Mather, Elihu Yale, James Oglethorpe, Benjamin Franklin, and Benjamin Thompson. And now, at the age of twenty-two, young "Macie" was recommended for membership in the Royal Society in these terms, signed by five of its illustrious members:

James Lewis Macie, Esq., M.A., late of Pembroke College, Oxford, and now of John Street, Golden Square,—a gentleman well versed in various branches of Natural Philosophy, and particularly in Chymistry and Mineralogy, being desirous of becoming a Fellow of the Royal Society, we whose names are hereunto subscribed do, from our personal knowledge of his merit, judge him highly worthy of that honor and likely to become a very useful and valuable member.

One of his sponsors was Henry Cavendish, the eccentric Englishman whose important researches in electrical and thermal physics, including the discovery of hydrogen, classify him as one of the leading scientists of the eighteenth century. Though Cavendish was thirty-four years older than Smithson, the two became intimate friends. His recommendation must have seemed to the young chemist almost as great an honor as election to the Society itself.

Another good friend was the eminent scientist Dr. William Hyde Wollaston, who later became secretary of the Royal Society.

On July 7, 1791, Smithson read his first scientific paper before the Society. It was entitled "An Account of Some Chemical Experiments on Tabasheer," tabasheer being a curious concretion found in the hollow of bamboo canes, and "an article of importance in the *materia medica* of the ancient Arabians, and still a medicine of great note in many parts of the East." The paper was published in the *Philosophical Transactions* of the Society for the year.

Thereafter he continued his experimentation with ardor. He made chemical analyses of the calamines and discovered and analyzed a new zinc ore, which is today called smithsonite in his honor; he subjected various members of the vegetable kingdom—violet, daisy, hollyhock, artichoke, currant, and many others—to minute chemical study. Indeed, it was his habit to analyze in this way practically everything that came to his notice, and for the purpose he equipped himself with a portable laboratory. He assembled a large collection of minerals and rare gems, many of them minute specimens, which when systematically labeled and classified enabled him to compare and readily identify other samples that came to hand. In justifying the value of such minute researches he had certainly a magnanimous viewpoint. In his thinking there was no hierarchy in nature. To him the star was no greater than the violet. "The particle and the planet," he said, "are subject to the same laws, and what is learned of the one will be known of the other." He would have agreed with Emerson:

> There is no great and no small
> To the Soul that maketh all.

Smithson's assiduity in matters of detail is illustrated by an anecdote related the year after his death in an address by Sir Davies Gilbert, president of the Royal Society. "Mr. Smithson declared," he said, "that happening to observe a tear gliding down a lady's cheek, he endeavored to catch it on a crystal vessel; that one-half of the drop escaped, but having preserved the other half he submitted it to reagents, and detected what was then called microcosmic salt, with muriate of soda, and, I think, three or four more saline substances, held in solution."

He published, in all, eight scientific papers in the Royal Society's *Philosophical Transactions* (1791-1817) and eighteen in Thomson's *Annals of Philosophy* (1819-25), a journal of high scientific eminence, and a short note in the *Philosophical Magazine* (1807).[3] As Spencer F. Baird described them, these articles "embrace a wide range of research, from the origin of the earth, the nature of the colors of the vegetables and insects, the analysis of minerals and chemicals, to an improved method of constructing lamps or of making coffee."

We have on record, furthermore, a statement of an American chemist with respect to the quality and value of Smithson's scientific contributions. Dr. Frank Wigglesworth Clarke (1847-1931), one-time chief chemist of the United States Geological Survey, expressed his opinion:

The most notable feature of Smithson's writings, from the standpoint of the modern analytical chemist, is the success obtained with the most primitive and unsatisfactory appliances. In Smithson's day, chemical apparatus was undeveloped, and instruments were improvised from such materials as lay readiest at hand. With such instruments, and with crude reagents, Smithson obtained analytical results of the most creditable character, and enlarged our knowledge of many mineral species. In his time the native carbonate and silicate of zinc were confounded as one species under the name "calomine"; but his researches distinguish between the two minerals, which are now known as smithsonite and calamine respectively.

To theory Smithson contributed little, if anything; but from a theoretical point of view the tone of his writings is singularly modern. His work was mostly done before Dalton

[3] In 1879, the fiftieth anniversary of Smithson's death, these twenty-seven papers, constituting his entire published scientific work, were collected and reprinted in volume 21 of the *Smithsonian Miscellaneous Collections*.

had announced the atomic theory, and yet Smithson saw clearly that a law of definite proportions must exist, although he did not attempt to account for it. His ability as a reasoner is best shown in his paper upon the Kirkdale bone cave, which Penn had sought to interpret by reference to the Noachian deluge. A clearer and more complete demolition of Penn's views could hardly be written today. Smithson was gentle with his adversary, but none the less thorough for all his moderation. He is not to be classed among the leaders of scientific thought; but his ability, and the usefulness of his contributions to knowledge, cannot be doubted.

Noteworthy, too, were his fidelity to the experimental method and his high regard for science in general. "It may be proper to say," he writes in one of his papers, "that the experiments have been stated *precisely* as they turned out, and have not been in the least degree bent to the system." He pursued his researches with the philosophic spirit of inquiry and with the accepted empirical methods. Although his scientific output was meager, and unlike his friend Cavendish he made no epoch-making discoveries, Smithson was great in scientific vision, and that is important to our understanding of his wishes to found an institution for the increase and diffusion of knowledge. But apart from that, he was, himself, an earnest seeker. "What we know in chemistry," he said, "bears so small a proportion to what we are ignorant of; our knowledge in every department of it is so incomplete, consisting so entirely of isolated points, thinly scattered, like lurid specks on a vast field of darkness, that no researches can be undertaken without producing some facts leading to consequences which extend beyond the boundaries of their immediate object." It was his modest ambition to enlarge these lurid specks.

Smithson never married, and so without family encumbrance and with a comfortable fortune he was free to travel about Europe, frequently on explorative tours, on which he collected minerals, rocks, and ores, or studied the physical features and climate of the country. He was a cosmopolitan and lived much of his life on the Continent —in Berlin, Paris, Florence, Geneva, and Rome. He once said that "the man of science is of no country, the world is his country, all mankind his countrymen." What friends he had were mostly scientists and writers. Scientific colleagues sent him their papers—Gay-Lussac, Marcet, Haüy, Berzelius, and Cordier. He associated and corresponded with such men as Wollaston, Davy, Gilbert, Biot, Klaproth, Black, Banks, and Thomson. Dominique François Arago, the eminent French astronomer and physicist, was an intimate friend.

Genesis of the Smithsonian Institution

ACTUALLY, so little is known about James Smithson's life that its recital in all possible detail would not fill many pages. We are bound to conclude that had it not been for the manner in which he disposed of his fortune, he would today be all but forgotten, notwithstanding his moderate achievement in science. He had wealth and evidently enjoyed entertaining his congenial friends and colleagues, but withal he was a lonely man. During his later years he lived in Paris at 121 Rue Montmartre. His health began to fail; the approach of old age and infirmity, added to his lifelong feeling that he had been cheated, offers a plausible explanation for his embitterment.

At one time, it is said, he intended to leave his money to the Royal Society, but because of a misunderstanding with the Society's council he changed his mind. Yet, as George Brown Goode said, "no one has been able to show why Smithson selected the United States as the seat of his foundation. He had no acquaintances in America, nor does he appear to have had any books relating to America except two. Rhees quotes from one of these [*Travels through North America,* by Isaac Weld, secretary of the Royal Society], a paragraph concerning Washington, then a small town of 5,000 inhabitants, in which it is predicted that 'the Federal city, as soon as navigation is perfected, will increase most rapidly, and that at a future day, if the affairs of the United States go on as rapidly as they have done, it will become the grand emporium of the West, and rival in magnitude and splendor the cities of the whole world.' "

One of Smithson's half-brothers, Earl Percy, who became the second Duke of Northumberland, fought in the American Revolutionary War. He came to Boston in 1774 in charge of a brigade, commanded the reinforcements at the Battle of Lexington, and led the column that reduced Fort Washington at Kings Bridge, N. Y., on November 16, 1776. He was advanced to the rank of lieutenant-general and returned to England in 1777. It is said that he was the first to suggest making peace with the colonists. We do not know that James Smithson ever fraternized with his relative; but Earl Percy's career at least suggests another tenuous link to America.

Smithson may have known the American patriot and poet Joel Barlow, who lived and traveled much abroad. It has been suggested, also, that Smithson may have "caught the first idea of his benevolent design" from Count Rumford (the American-born Benjamin Thompson), who in 1800 had founded the Royal Institution of London.

But aside from these uncertain hints, we are left in the dark. It is most reasonable to suppose, however, that America appealed to him in the same way as it did to certain romantic poets of his day—Coleridge, Shelley, and Blake, for example. America was a country where every man had an equal chance and where birthrights were not annulled by the bar sinister.

If we are to believe his friend Arago's recorded statement, Smithson in his later days took up gambling to an extent that sometimes worried his distinguished friend. "Save for a few hours given to repose," his life, wrote Arago, "was regularly divided between the most interesting scientific researches and gaming. It was a source of great regret to me that this learned experimentalist should devote half of so valuable a life to a course so little in harmony with an intellect whose wonderful powers called forth the admiration of the world around him." It is not recorded that he ever lost any great amount in excess of his winnings (perhaps his friend's remonstrances held him somewhat in check), but it is clear that he did have the old itch to play with his money, and it probably afforded him considerable diversion and some relief from his increasing physical and mental sufferings.

On October 23, 1826, Smithson, at the time residing in London, made his historic will, drawn in his own hand in the terse and deliberate language of one who knew well what he was doing. Because this will was, as it turned out, so epoch-making a document in the history of science, the complete text of it is here given:

The Will of James Smithson

I James Smithson Son to Hugh, first Duke of Northumberland, & Elizabeth, Heiress of the Hungerfords of Studley, & Niece to Charles the proud Duke of Somerset, now residing in Bentinck Street, Cavendish Square, do this twenty-third day of October, one thousand eight hundred and twenty-six, make this my last Will and Testament:

I bequeath the whole of my property of every nature & kind soever to my bankers, Messrs. Drummonds of Charing Cross, in trust, to be disposed of in the following manner, and I desire of my said Executors to put my property under the management of the Court of Chancery.

To John Fitall, formerly my Servant, but now employed in the London Docks, and residing at No. 27, Jubilee Place, North Mile End, old town, in consideration of his attachment & fidelity to me, & the long & great care he has taken of my effects, & my having done but very little for him, I give and bequeath the Annuity or annual sum of One hundred pounds sterling for his life, to be paid to him quarterly, free of legacy duty & all other deductions, the first payment to be made to him at the expiration of three months after my death. I have at divers times lent sums of money to Henry Honore Sailly, formerly my Servant, but now keeping the Hungerford Hotel in the rue Caumartin at Paris, & for which sums of money I have undated bills or bonds signed by him. Now, I will & direct that if he desires it, these sums of money be let remain in his hands at an Interest of five per cent. for five years after the date of the present Will.

To Henry James Hungerford, my Nephew, heretofore called Henry James Dickinson, son of my late brother, Lieutenant-Colonel Henry Louis Dickinson, now residing with Mr. Auboin, at Bourg la Reine, near Paris, I give and bequeath for his life the whole of the income arising from my property of every nature & kind whatever, after the payment of the above Annuity, & after the death of John Fitall, that Annuity likewise, the payments to be made to him at the time of the interest or dividends becomes due on the Stocks or other property from which the income arises.

Should the said Henry James Hungerford have a child or children, legitimate or illegitimate, I leave to such child or children, his or their heirs, executors, & assigns, after the death of his, or her, or their Father, the whole of my property of every kind absolutely & forever, to be divided between them, if there is more than one, in the manner their father shall judge proper, or, in case of his omitting to decide this, as the Lord Chancellor shall judge proper.

Should my said Nephew, Henry James Hungerford, marry, I empower him to make a jointure.

In the case of the death of my said Nephew without leaving a child or children, or the death of the child or children he may have had under the age of twenty-one years or intestate, I then bequeath the whole of my property subject to the Annuity of One Hundred pounds to John Fitall, & for the security & payment of which I mean Stock to remain in this Country, to the United States of America, to found at Washington, under the name of the Smithsonian Institution, an Establishment for the increase & diffusion of knowledge among men.

I think it proper here to state, that all the money which will be standing in the French five per cents. at my death in the names of the father of my above mentioned Nephew, Henry James Hungerford, & all that in my names, is the property of my said Nephew, being what he inherited from his

12

father, or what I have laid up for him from the savings upon his income.

In this document the Smithsonian Institution had its origin. James Smithson died in Genoa, Italy, on June 26, 1829, at the age of sixty-four, and six years later his nephew, Henry James Hungerford (then known as Baron Eunice de la Batut), also died. And as destiny would have it, Hungerford died unmarried and without heirs, leaving operative the final provision of Smithson's will. The manner in which that provision was carried out is the burden of this book.

2

INTERLUDE

ONE HUNDRED and twenty years have now passed since James Smithson died in Genoa. He was buried there in a tomb in the little cemetery belonging to the English Church. We are told that it was a beautiful but solitary spot planted with cypress trees and situated on the Heights of San Benigno overlooking the Gulf of Genoa. Though on alien soil, it seemed a not incongruous resting place for this man who had lived the lonely and frustrated life that circumstances dealt him.

In 1891 the Secretary of the Smithsonian, Samuel P. Langley, visited Smithson's tomb and on behalf of the Institution arranged for the perpetual care of the grave. On a later visit Langley placed at the tomb a bronze tablet with a bas-relief of Smithson and another at the English Church. Up to this time the tomb bore no reference to Smithson as the founder of the Smithsonian Institution, though there had been a monument erected by his nephew, "in token of gratitude to a generous benefactor and as a tribute to departed worth." The tablet placed at the tomb was afterward stolen.

Late in 1900 Secretary Langley received word from one of the officials of the English Church at Genoa that the cemetery on the San Benigno Heights was in danger of having to be moved, because of encroachment of a municipal stone quarry, "which was slowly but surely eating its way toward us from the sea through the rocky side of the hill on which we stand." What was to be done with James Smithson's remains? "Are they," inquired the letter, "to be laid with all possible care and reverence in new ground here, or are they to be conveyed to the United States?"

At first the Smithsonian Board of Regents thought it best to arrange for their reinterment at Genoa, but when it was learned definitely, just three years later, that the Italian authorities had actually expropriated the old cemetery and that it certainly was to be demolished, it was proposed to have the remains brought to America. This was urged particularly by the distinguished inventor Alexander Graham Bell, then one of the Regents. Consequently, Bell was appointed as a committee to take charge of the matter, and on December 15, 1903, with Mrs. Bell, he sailed for Europe on his memorable mission.

They arrived in Genoa on Christmas Day, and the removal was consummated without delay. Undisturbed for three-quarters of a century, the Smithson tomb was opened on December 31, 1903, in the presence of Bell, the United States consul, and six other witnesses. "I was surprised," Bell is quoted as saying,[1] "at the remarkable state in which the body was found. The skeleton was complete. The skull was that of an intellectual man. The bones had separated, but they did not crumble when exposed to the air."

On January 2, 1904, fitting ceremonies were held, after which the Smithson remains, in a new metal casket and a strong wooden coffin, were put aboard the steamer *Princess Irene* of the North German Lloyd Line. After a stormy but otherwise uneventful passage, they arrived in New York on the night of January 19. The United States

1 *Washington Post,* January 24, 1904.

steamer *Dolphin,* by direction of President Theodore Roosevelt, completed the transport to the Navy Yard in Washington, D. C., arriving on Saturday, the 23d.

On Monday morning the coffin, draped in American and British flags, was borne from the Navy Yard through the city, accompanied by a troop of the Fifteenth Cavalry from Fort Myer, Va., the Marine Band, and a detachment of Marines, and deposited in the center of the main hall of the Smithsonian Building. A distinguished company had gathered to pay honor to James Smithson, and appropriate and impressive ceremonies were conducted.

It was agreed that Smithson's remains should have their final resting place somewhere in the grounds of the Institution. While the site was being pondered, the original tomb from Italy was sent for. When this arrived late in 1904, however, it was found to be a very modest structure and thought to be insufficient for an exterior site. On March 6, 1905, Secretary Langley reported to the Board of Regents that "he had hoped that at some future time Congress would make an adequate appropriation for giving these remains a fitting interment, but that so far as he had been able he had given present effect to the mandate of the Board by depositing them temporarily within the building in a small room which he had fitted up on the immediate left of the north entrance to the building." At the conclusion of this meeting the Board proceeded to the room and witnessed the deposit of the casket and the sealing of the tomb.

In the small mortuary chapel today still lie the remains of James Smithson, whose faith in the then young republic, the United States of America, was the inception of a great scientific institution. His boast and prophesy—"my name will live in the memory of man when the titles of the Northumberlands and Percys are extinct and forgotten"—perhaps is not yet entirely fulfilled, but certainly his name is known, *per orbem,* by millions who may never have heard who he was.

3

WHAT TO DO WITH HALF A MILLION DOLLARS

The Legacy Claimed

THE NEWS that the United States of America had fallen heir to an estate worth £100,000 was not, as it might be today, flashed around the world in the twinkling of an eye. Henry James Hungerford, Smithson's nephew and heir, died on the 5th of June, 1835, and the first announcement of the Smithson bequest to the United States was not received by the American Government until July 28, seven weeks later. On December 17, 1835, formal recognition of the gift was made by President Andrew Jackson in a message to Congress, but he had no authority, he said, to take any steps toward accepting it. There then began in Congress a tedious ten-year proceeding and debate concerning the manner of consummating the bequest and the form in which Smithson's institution should be established.

In the Senate the matter was referred to the Committee on the Judiciary, and resolutions were offered providing for the prosecution of the claim. The committee believed that Mr. Smithson's bequest was a valid one and "that the United States would be entertained in the court of chancery of England to assert their claim to the fund as trustees for the purpose of founding the charitable institution at Washington to which it is destined by the donor." There were dissensions. W. C. Preston, of South Carolina, thought that Smithson's intention was to found a university, but that the United States had no power to receive the money. John C. Calhoun expressed the opinion that "it was beneath their dignity to receive presents from anyone." But others, including James Buchanan, of Pennsylvania, advocated acceptance, and eventually, on May 2, 1836, the resolution to do so passed the Senate.

In the House of Representatives the matter of the Smithson gift was laid before a special committee under the chairmanship of John Quincy Adams, who had already served his country as Senator and as President and now at the age of sixty-nine was serving as Representative in Congress from Massachusetts. Adams saw in the action of James Smithson a far-reaching potential. He succeeded by his eloquence in overcoming the House opposition and successfully steered the passage of the House bill. The actions of the Senate and the House were combined in one bill, which the President signed on July 1, 1836, authorizing the prosecution of the claim. An appropriation of $10,000 was made to cover the costs.

Accordingly, the President appointed the Honorable Richard Rush, of Pennsylvania, as agent of the Government to go to London and "assert the claim of the United States." Mr. Rush was the son of Dr. Benjamin Rush, a signer of the Declaration of Independence, and was a man experienced in finance as well as in matters of diplomacy. He had been Comptroller of the United States Treasury, Attorney General, Minister to England, Secretary of the Treasury, and Minister to France. He "knew

18

his way around," and a better choice could not have been made. Considerable difficulties were encountered in expediting the claim through the court of chancery, which Mr. Rush soon found was some eight hundred cases in arrears. It is to his everlasting credit, however, that he was able by diligence and adroitness to jump the legal hurdles and bring the friendly suit to a comparatively speedy conclusion. In less than two years he had seen the thing through. As was well said at the time, "Had he not urged them to the top of their speed, he would have had a lighter weight of gold to carry home with him." As it was, the estate of Smithson transferred to Mr. Rush consisted of securities worth more than £106,000 sterling. When the costs of the suit had been deducted, the remainder was converted into gold sovereigns, and on July 17, 1838, packed in £1,000 bags in eleven boxes, it was shipped aboard the packet *Mediator* for New York, where it arrived on August 29. Three days later, the gold, amounting to £104,960 8s. 6d., was delivered to the United States Mint in Philadelphia and recoined into American money. It amounted to $508,318.46.

Congressional Action

JUST WHAT the Smithsonian Institution was to be, however, was as much unsettled as ever. On December 6, 1838, Martin Van Buren, who in 1837 had succeeded Andrew Jackson as President, formally announced to Congress that the Smithson fund had been duly received and reminded the legislators of "the obligation now devolving upon the United States to fulfill the object of the bequest." But Congress, it seems, was faced with more pressing problems, for the nation was passing through the worst economic depression it had known, the Panic of 1837. There had been over-expansion in industry; the widespread canal-building enterprises were not paying off; the working classes were restless; poverty was rampant. The legislators were trying desperately to bring the country out of its economic doldrums, and it is no wonder that they took eight years to determine the disposal of James Smithson's half-million-dollar gift. In those days, half a million dollars was considered a good-sized sum of money; endowment funds for educational, charitable, and scientific purposes had not reached the staggering sums that we know today. So Congress took its time.

We must remember that Smithson's unique gift had taken the country by surprise. Furthermore, Congress had little precedent to follow, for in all the land there were but three scientific foundations that pretended to be national in scope. These were the American Philosophical Society, at Philadelphia, patterned after the Royal Society and dating from the time of Benjamin Franklin; the American Academy of Arts and Sciences, at Boston, established directly after the Revolution; and the Franklin Institute, at Philadelphia, organized in 1824. There were also a few private scientific establishments, such as Bartram's Botanic Garden, Rittenhouse's Observatory, and Peale's Natural History Museum, and a number of local scientific societies in the larger cities. In the Government itself science had made but a small beginning in the United States Coast Survey, proposed by Jefferson in 1807.

It is true that science had not advanced too rapidly in the new republic, but the country could refer with pride to Franklin and Jefferson. With slightly less esteem it could point out such men of science as Thomas Cooper, Constantine Samuel Rafinesque, and Thomas Say—all to die within the decade 1830-40. Also there was a young man, Joseph Henry, then a teacher at the College of New Jersey, who was to have much to say and do concerning American science. And scientific matters now were coming more and more to the attention of Congress and the people. Samuel F. B. Morse had just applied for a patent on his telegraph and had asked the Government for $30,000 to subsidize a fifty-mile demonstration telegraph system. The lawmakers took five years to approve this appropriation, but it developed into a truly far-sighted investment in the country's future. Many other inventions were claiming public attention, and although it cannot be denied that science still had its stronghold in Europe, it was also true that America was particularly responsive to the wave of intellectual activity that seemed to be coming its way.

The Smithson bequest, operating somewhat fortuitously, coincided with this wave. In the House of Representatives John Quincy Adams, who possessed an abiding and militant devotion to science, again took the lead and was made chairman of the nine-man committee to which the Smithson matter was referred. Adams had strong convictions on the subject and was especially opposed to the idea that any of the money should be used for "the endowment of any school, college, university, or ecclesiastical establishment." Instead, he thought that Smithson's wishes would best be carried out by the creation of an astronomical observatory, with instruments and a library. The "university" idea, however, was favored by many, including such leading men of the country as President Francis Wayland, of Brown University, and it seemed for a while it would win. The Honorable Asher Robbins, of Rhode Island, in an eloquent speech before the Senate on January 10, 1839, proposed the creation of "an institution of which there is no model either in this country or Europe, to provide such a course of education and discipline as would give to the faculties of the human mind an improvement far beyond what they afterwards attain in any of the professional pursuits." This was fine, but it certainly was not very definite, and the matter was tabled until the following session of Congress.

The next year Mr. Adams brought up the subject again, and on March 5, 1840, he reviewed the whole case before the House in an elaborate report and again argued strongly against the creation of a school or college. "We should in no case," he said, "avail ourselves of a stranger's munificence to rear our children." He still favored the observatory plan, but could effect no conclusive action of any kind at that session, although debate continued and alternate proposals were made. Another year passed, and another new President, William Henry Harrison, Virginia-born Ohioan, took office but died of pneumonia only a month after his inauguration. He was succeeded by Vice President John Tyler, and the Smithsonian question was one of the "headaches" he inherited.

It is no wonder that those most interested in the Smithsonian Institution began to despair. On November 26, 1841, Richard Rush wrote to his friend and former secretary Benjamin Ogle Tayloe: "Alas for the Smithsonian Institution! I labored anxiously and hard for the *fund,* and after receiving the full gold on the other side of the water, more in value than the original bequest, through the fortunate sale I made of the English Government stock, in which the testator's money stood, never lost sight of it until it was all safely deposited in the United States Mint; little dreaming, however, that there the matter was to rest for years. But so it seems,—so it was, and fortunate will it be if the fund itself, at an era of such dishonesty and hocus-pocus, is not made way with, or dilapidated, before any public use whatever is made of the beneficent bequest. Congress has slept over the subject, and the Executive too. . . ."

Not until 1844 did much progress seem to be made. On June 6, a definite proposal came in the form of a bill from the Joint Library Committee of Congress, providing that the original amount of the Smithson bequest be considered as a permanent loan to the United States at 6 per cent interest; that the interest that had accrued up to July 1, 1844 ($178,604), be used for the erection of buildings and the enclosure of grounds for the Smithsonian Institution; that the business of the establishment should be conducted by a board of twelve managers from different states or territories; that a plain and substantial building be erected, with rooms for a museum, library, chemical laboratory, lectures, and arboretum; and that all objects of natural history belonging to the United States in Washington be transferred to the Institution. It provided further that a superintendent should be appointed who would also be "professor" of agriculture and horticulture. There would be additional "professors" of natural history, chemistry, astronomy, etc. Experiments would be made to determine the utility of new fruits, plants, and vegetables. Students would be admitted free. These provisions were amplified in another bill introduced in the Senate on December 12, and another period of discussion began. In a brilliant speech the eminent jurist Rufus Choate of Massachusetts opposed the school or college idea as being too utilitarian and unnecessary, but approved the lecture and library provisions of the bill. "Does not the whole history of civilization concur to declare that a various and ample library is one of the surest, most constant, most permanent and most economical instrumentalities to increase and diffuse knowledge?" He would like to see Smithson's gift used to accumulate a grand and noble public library, equal to any in the world, and he would amend the bill accordingly. The pros and cons argued for a few days longer, and on January 23, 1845, the Senate passed the bill. It was sent to the House, but there in the hurry of a short session of Congress, it was once again left undisposed of.

The following year a new bill, embracing the principal features of the old but adding several new provisions, was sponsored by Robert Dale Owen of Indiana. The new bill contained a section providing for a sort of normal school to train school teachers, to qualify teachers in natural science and in "the most useful of all modern sciences—the humble yet world-subduing science of primary education." The library provision was retained. Scientific research was to be encouraged. Publications in science and history, pamphlets, magazines, manuals, etc., were authorized. Mr. Owen made an impassioned plea for his bill and took the Congressmen to task for their dilatoriness in handling the Smithson bequest. The debate opened again in full force. George W. Jones and Andrew

Johnson of Tennessee and Orlando B. Ficklin of Illinois attacked the Owen bill, but just as vigorously Jefferson Davis of Mississippi, Frederick P. Stanton of Tennessee, and Joseph R. Ingersoll of Pennsylvania defended it. Various amendments were offered. The provisions for a normal school, professors, lecturers, and students were stricken out. The provision for lectures was rejected. The annual appropriation for the library was increased. An amendment was adopted specifying that the Government collections deposited in the institution should be known as the National Museum. Finally, a substitute bill was agreed upon, and the House passed it by the rather close vote of eighty-five to seventy-six. In August the Senate considered the bill and passed it by a vote of twenty-six to thirteen. It was signed by President James K. Polk on August 10, 1846. The Smithsonian Institution was at last established—twenty years after James Smithson drew his will.

The Institution Established

As it was finally passed, the organic act establishing the Smithsonian contained eleven sections:

(1) Setting up the Smithsonian Establishment;
(2) Providing for the disposition of the Smithsonian funds;
(3) Providing for a Board of Regents, Chancellor, Executive Committee, and Secretary;
(4) Providing for the selection of a site for the Smithsonian Building;
(5) Providing for the erection of the building;
(6) Transferring to the Institution all objects of art, natural history, etc., belonging to the United States in Washington and also the minerals, books, manuscripts, and other property of James Smithson, which had been received by the Government;
(7) Outlining certain duties of the Secretary and providing for salaries;
(8) Authorizing stated and special meetings of members of the Institution and specifying that an appropriation not

exceeding an average of $25,000 a year, from the interest of the Smithsonian fund, be made for the gradual formation of a library;

(9) Authorizing the managers of the Institution to spend income of the Smithson fund "as they deem best suited for the promotion of the purpose of James Smithson";

(10) Directing that one copy of all publications copyrighted under the acts of Congress shall be deposited in the Smithsonian Library and one copy in the Library of Congress;

(11) Reserving the right of Congress to alter, amend, add to, or repeal any of the provisions of the act.

The first Board of Regents was constituted as follows:

George M. Dallas, of Pennsylvania, Vice President of the United States, *ex officio*

Roger B. Taney, of Maryland, Chief Justice of the United States, *ex officio*

William W. Seaton, Mayor of the City of Washington, *ex officio*

Senators George Evans, of Maine; Isaac S. Pennybacker, of Virginia; and Sidney Breese, of Illinois, appointed by the President of the Senate

Representatives William J. Hough, of New York; Robert Dale Owen, of Indiana; and Henry W. Hilliard, of Alabama, appointed by the Speaker of the House

Rufus Choate, of Massachusetts; Gideon Hawley, of New York; Richard Rush, of Pennsylvania; and William C. Preston, of South Carolina, citizens of states, elected by Congress

Alexander Dallas Bache and Joseph G. Totten, members of the National Institute, citizens of Washington, D. C.

Now that the legal difficulties were over, little time was lost in getting the new organization moving. On September 7, 1846, at the first meeting of the Board of Regents, Vice President Dallas was elected Chancellor of the Institution; on December 3, Joseph Henry was elected Secretary; and on December 4, the Board of Regents adopted Henry's plan of organization.

JOSEPH HENRY BUILDS AN INSTITUTION

The Scene in 1846

THE YEAR 1846 has been called "the year of decision," and, indeed, it is surprising to note the number of important events in the history of our country which revolve around that date. It was an exciting period, a time of "manifest destiny." Things were happening at an appalling rate—appalling, perhaps, to a republic barely three score and ten years of age. As a nation we were suffering growth pains. We were expanding toward the Pacific, treading on the claims of other countries. In 1846, after several years of heated contest, our argument with Great Britain over the Oregon boundary was settled by treaty, adding to our territory the land that now comprises Washington, Oregon, and Idaho, and parts of Montana and Wyoming. On our southern border we had engaged in another controversy, which led in 1846 to war with Mexico. By terms of the treaty two years later we gained the area now included in California, Arizona,

PLATE 3. Tomb of James Smithson at Genoa, Italy, before it
was removed to the United States

PLATE 4. Tomb of James Smithson after removal to the
Smithsonian Building in Washington

PLATE 5. Joseph Henry, first secretary of the
Smithsonian Institution, 1846-1878

PLATE 6. Joseph Henry's electromagnet

PLATE 7. Statue of Joseph Henry in front of the Smithsonian Building in Washington. Sculptor, William Wetmore Story

Utah, and New Mexico. Congressmen were debating the Wilmot Proviso which would forever outlaw slavery and involuntary servitude "in any part of territory acquired from Mexico."

John C. Frémont had completed his explorations and conquests beyond the Mississippi, and the year before (1845) the Senate had published his reports describing the new country and its possibilities. One of his thousands of readers, we are told, was Brigham Young, who thereby was inspired to lead his zealous band of Mormons westward in 1847 into the "Promised Land," the Great Salt Lake country.

The boundaries of knowledge, too, were expanding. In 1846 William T. G. Morton, a Boston dentist, demonstrated the successful use of anesthesia in surgery, of which the British medical journal *Lancet* said, "Next to the discovery of Franklin, it is the second and greatest contribution of the New World to science." Two years earlier, Samuel F. B. Morse, applying the electromagnetic discoveries of Michael Faraday and Joseph Henry, demonstrated the practicability of the telegraph, which was soon to revolutionize commercial communication. Only a few years later both anesthesia and telegraphy were to prove their humanitarian usefulness in the War between the States. The year 1846, too, was the time of two other important American inventions: the sewing machine of Elias Howe and the rotary printing press of Richard Marsh Hoe.

These were spectacular discoveries, definitely changing the trend of men's lives and occupations. Other important but less sensational scientific events were also taking place. John James Audubon, the ornithologist and artist, had just completed and seen through the press his last major work, *The Viviparous Quadrupeds of North America,* in collaboration with his friend the Reverend John Bachman. In Boston there arrived from Switzerland in 1846 the learned Louis Agassiz, who became America's most popular scientist and most memorable teacher and who wielded an influence in the natural sciences that was not to pass for several generations. Exploration was receiving significant impetus. The United States Exploring Expedition, under the command of Capt. Charles Wilkes, had returned in 1842 after four years in the South Seas and Antarctic regions with exciting things to tell. From scattered parts of the world it had brought back extensive collections of zoological and geological specimens, which would furnish scientific stimuli for many years. Likewise, scholars would utilize the findings of John C. Frémont and his small party, who explored the South Pass to California, and defined the geography, botany, geology, astronomy, and meteorology of the region.

Joseph Henry's Background

SUCH were the men and events that set the stage for Joseph Henry, the first Secretary and the organizing "architect" of the Smithsonian Institution.

"Joseph Henry," wrote the astronomer Simon Newcomb, "was the first American after Franklin to reach high eminence as an original investigator in physical science." Though only forty-nine years old when chosen to head the Smithsonian, he had already made a reputation as a physicist through his great discoveries in electromagnetism, and at that time he was perhaps America's most distinguished scientist. The Smithsonian Board of Regents, however, had set their mark high. They wanted, they resolved, a man possessing weight of character as well as a high grade of talent. He must possess "eminent scientific and general requirements." He must be capable of "advancing science and promoting letters by original research and effort, well qualified to act as a respected channel of communication between the Institution and scientific and literary individuals and societies in this and foreign countries." Furthermore, he must have efficiency as an executive officer and a knowledge of the world. Henry was their man.

When he was requested to take over the direction of the new institution, Henry was serving as professor of natural philosophy in the College of New Jersey (now Princeton University). He had been there since the fall of 1832, happily situated, since he was able to carry on the researches he had begun while associated with the Albany Academy. Furthermore, he enjoyed teaching, was well liked at Princeton, and had little reason for desiring a change.

Descended from Scotch Puritans who had settled in eastern New York state about the time of the American Revolution, Joseph Henry grew up around Albany, where he was born on December 17, 1797. Although Henry was to become an eminent scientist, his first leanings were not in that direction at all, but toward literature.[1] Early in life he developed a fondness for the theatre and might well have become an actor. As a youngster he seemed not particularly studious, and for a while was apprenticed to a watchmaker to supplement the family's meager income.

[1] Mary A. Henry, in her unpublished diary [in the Smithsonian Archives] covering the years 1858 to 1868, recounts an amusing anecdote of her father that shows him to have been a boy possessing normal juvenile ambitions but with perhaps an unusual degree of inventiveness. On May 26, 1865, Miss Henry wrote: "At night Father gave us a little incident of his boyhood which interested us. He said that a certain man in the village where he lived with his grandmother—it was a shoemaker I believe—annoyed him greatly by passing his hand roughly over his face, bending up his nose in the process and causing him considerable pain. He was a slight, delicate boy but determined to discover some means of self-defence. He at length hit upon the following expedient—his first experiment as he says in practical mechanics. At the approach of his tormentor he threw himself upon the ground and as the man stooped over him to seize him he caught hold of [his] ankles and placing his feet in his stomach with one dexterous kick sent him over backwards. He tried the same experiment several times upon some young men who were in the habit of teasing him, and greatly to the amusement and admiration of the bystanders. He mentioned during the conversation that his first ambition was to be a chimney sweeper. He had watched a certain individual somewhat his senior ascend his grandmother's chimney and was inspired with the greatest admiration for the calling. There was a small space between his grandmother's house and that of the next neighbor and his clothes suffered greatly in consequence of his efforts to [crawl] between the two walls chimney-sweep fashion."

29

When he was about sixteen, however, his attention was accidentally directed to a book containing *Lectures on Experimental Philosophy, Astronomy, and Chemistry, Intended Chiefly for the Use of Young People,* by an English clergyman, the Reverend George Gregory. His interest was so seriously and strongly aroused that he determined to make the pursuit of these matters of "natural philosophy" the great object of his life. He began to study, first at a night school and then at the Albany Academy, earning his way by teaching a country school and later tutoring to the family of General Stephen Van Rensselaer, of patroon fame, and also to Henry James, the elder, at that time a pupil at the Academy.[2] Next he participated in a road-surveying expedition across the western part of New York from West Point to Lake Erie; this trip served both to provide some valuable experience and to fortify his somewhat precarious health. When he returned he was engaged as a teacher at Albany Academy, and in 1828, at the age of thirty-one, he was appointed professor of mathematics. In May 1830 he was married to his cousin Harriet L. Alexander, of Schenectady. Two years later he was called to Princeton.

Henry's Early Scientific Research

THE NEXT TEN YEARS were fruitful ones—both for Joseph Henry and for American science. In addition to his courses

2 The principal of the school, who was a chemist, encouraged his students to play at science under the leadership of the young Henry. Perhaps in seeking an answer to the question "Why does flame or smoke always mount upward?" Henry taught his charges to fly hot-air balloons, supplied with lighted balls of tow. When one of these balls accidentally entered the window of a neighbor's barn, Henry James was seriously burned in an attempt to stamp it out. The result was two years in bed and a double amputation of his leg above the knee.

The association of Henry and James was continued in later years and they became intimate friends. In 1837 they traveled together for some months in Europe. In the early 1840's when James was searching for a reconciliation between religion and science and had taken up residence in New York he frequently saw Henry.

and lectures in physics and mathematics, chemistry, mineralogy, and geology, he was able to conduct his own experiments that were to prove epochal. Let us summarize briefly Henry's scientific researches up to the time that he went to Washington. Conveniently, such a summary is provided by Henry himself in a letter dated December 4, 1876, and addressed to the Reverend Samuel B. Dod, of Princeton. He divides his account into sixteen parts, which are here somewhat condensed but given essentially in Henry's own phrasing:

1. Previous to leaving Albany, he says, he made a series of experiments on electromagnetism in which he developed the principles of the electromagnet and applied the magnetic power produced in the invention of the first electromagnetic machine; that is, a mechanical contrivance by which electromagnetism was applied as a motive power.[3] Also, while in Albany, he applied the results of his experiments to the first electromagnetic telegraph, in which signals were transmitted by exciting an electromagnet, located some distance away, which struck bells in succession.

At Princeton he continued his experiments and constructed a still more powerful electromagnet—one that would lift over 3,000 pounds—and with it illustrated to his students how, by means of a relay-magnet, a large

[3] Early use of the electromagnet industrially is described by Elmer Eugene Barker in "The Story of Crown Point Iron" in *New York History* (1942). Writing of the Penfield Ironworks at Crown Point, N. Y., he says: "Had the knowledge of generating and using hydroelectric power been available to industry at that time, doubtless electric separators would have been used at the Penfield forge, as the proprietors were enterprising, intelligent men, who were on the first line of industrial advance in their times. In the year 1831 they had secured an electromagnet from Professor Henry of the Albany Academy. . . . It was probably the first industrial use of electricity anywhere. This primitive device was worked by a wet battery or 'galvanic cell' as it was then called. It was used here for recharging the bar magnets of the separator, and also, it has been said, for separating iron and steel from brass and copper scrap metal." Mr. Barker refers to Rice's *Biography of Thomas Davenport* for the part played by this Crown Point electromagnet in the experiments of Davenport leading to his invention of the electric motor.

amount of such power might be called into operation at a distance of many miles.

Just before leaving on a trip to England in 1837 he again turned his attention to the telegraph. The first actual line of telegraph using the earth as a conductor, he says, was made in the beginning of 1836. A wire was stretched across the front campus of the college grounds, from the upper story of the library to the hall opposite, with the ends terminating in two wells. Through this wire signals were sent from his house to his laboratory. [Here Henry interpolates a short account of the history of the invention of the telegraph, claiming that the electromagnetic telegraph was invented by him in Albany in 1830, two years, he says, before Morse conceived the idea and seven years before he attempted to carry his idea into practice. He states that he did not take out a patent on his invention, as he was urged to do, because he did not consider it compatible with the dignity of science to confine the benefits that might be derived from it to the exclusive use of any individual. He reiterates that he was the first to bring the electromagnet into the condition necessary to its use in telegraphy and to point out its application to the telegraph. He gives Morse great credit, however, for his alphabet and for his perseverance in bringing the telegraph into practical use. The fact remains, however, that Morse was issued a patent for the invention of the telegraph on June 20, 1840. Just how much credit is due Joseph Henry will perhaps never be fully settled.]

2. His next experiment concerned what he called "electrodynamic induction." In 1831 Michael Faraday had discovered that when a current of electricity was passed through a wire from a battery, a current in an opposite direction was induced in a wire arranged parallel to this conductor. Henry discovered that induction of a similar kind took place in the primary conducting wire itself, so that although a current in passing through a short wire conductor would produce no sparks or shocks, if the wire

were long enough both of these effects would be produced. By using as a conductor a flat ribbon, covered with silk, rolled into a spiral form, he found that brilliant sparks and other electrical effects of high intensity could be produced from a battery of low intensity.

3. Afterward he made a series of investigations that resulted in producing inductive currents of different orders, of different directions, and made up of waves alternately in opposite directions. He found, also, that a metal plate of any kind, placed between two conductors, neutralized this induction, and that this effect was due to a current in the plate itself. Further, he observed that a current of quantity was capable of producing a current of intensity, and vice versa.

4. He also demonstrated that electrodynamic induction with ordinary electricity could be produced at a remarkable distance. If a current were sent through a wire on the outside of a building, electrical effects were produced in a parallel wire inside the building. He found also that the induced current appeared to change its direction with the distance of the two wires and that the discharge of electricity from a Leyden jar is of an oscillatory character.

5. His next experiment related to "atmospheric induction," reminiscent of Benjamin Franklin's experiment in drawing lightning from the clouds. In this he used two large kites, with the lower end of the string (consisting of fine wire) of one attached to the upper surface of the other, and the end of the whole coiled around an insulated drum. When the sky was perfectly clear the kites were flown, and sparks were drawn, said Henry, of "surprising intensity and pungency, the electricity being supplied from the air, and the intensity being attributed to the induction of the long wire on itself."

6. A related experiment was made on induction from thunder clouds. Using his tin roof as an induction plate, he soldered a wire to the edge of the roof, passed it into his study and out again through holes in the window sash, and fastened the other end to a metal plate in a deep

well in front of his house. By breaking the circuit of that part of the wire in the study and inserting in the opening a magnetized spiral, needles placed in this were magnetized by a flash of lightning so far away that the thunder could scarcely be heard. He found, also, that the electrical disturbance thus produced was oscillatory in character; the discharge first passed through the wire from the roof to the well, then one occurred in the opposite direction, and so on until equilibrium was restored.

7. This experiment led to a series of experiments with lightning rods which contributed greatly to our understanding of the nature of electricity. It was shown, among other phenomena, that when a powerful electrical charge such as lightning is transmitted through a portion of air, the air along the path of the discharge is "endowed for a moment with an intense repulsive energy. . . . It is to this repulsive energy, or tendency in air to expand at right angles to the path of a stroke of lightning, that the mechanical effects which accompany the latter are generally to be attributed."

8. Another series of Henry's investigations pertained to "the phosphorogenic emanation from the sun," in which he extended the list of known substances "which possess the capability of exhibiting phosphorescence" when exposed to electric discharge.

9. A new method of determining the velocity of projectiles was the subject of his next inquiry. The principle involved in this was "the instantaneous transmission of electrical action to determine the time of the passage of a ball between two screens, placed at a short distance from each other in the path of the projectile. . . . The observer is provided with a revolving cylinder moving by clock-work at a uniform rate, and of which the convex surface is divided into equal parts indicating a fractional part of a second. The passage of the ball through the screen breaks a galvanic circuit, the time of which is indicated on the revolving cylinder by the terminal spark produced in a wire surrounding a bundle of iron wires."

10. In collaboration with his brother-in-law, Stephen Alexander, Princeton professor of astronomy, Henry experimented to determine the relative heat of different parts of the sun's disk. It was shown that the sunspots radiated less heat than the adjacent parts and that all parts of the sun's surface did not radiate an equal amount of heat.

11. Another experiment was made with what was called a thermal telescope, which consisted of a long hollow cone of pasteboard, lined with silver leaf and painted outside with lampblack. The angle at the cone's apex was such as to cause all the parallel rays from a distant object entering the larger end to be reflected onto the end of a thermopile, which was connected with a galvanometer. When the axis of the conical reflector was directed toward a distant object of greater or less temperature than the surrounding bodies, such as a horse, the difference was immediately indicated by the needle of the galvanometer. When the instrument was directed toward the sky, to different clouds, and to the moon, various conclusions as to radiant heat could be drawn.

12. Further studies of radiant heat were made "to examine the nature of the fact mentioned by Count Rumford that balls of clay introduced into a fire under some conditions increase the heat given off into an apartment." He concluded that the "increase in the radiant heat, which would facilitate the roasting of an article before the fire, would be at the expense of the boiling of a liquid in a vessel suspended directly over the point of combustion."

13. In another investigation, pertaining to the diffusion of metals, he demonstrated that mercury could be siphoned up through a three-foot piece of thick lead wire, and proved that solid silver would dissolve in solid copper.

14. He investigated the constitution of matter with reference to its "liquidity" and "solidity," concluding that "rigidity differs from liquidity more in a polarity which prevents slipping of the molecules than in a difference of the attractive force with which the molecules are held

together." Heating a liquid, he said, does not neutralize the attraction of the molecules but rather neutralizes the polarity of the molecules so as to give them "perfect freedom of motion around any imaginable axis." He explained that the reason that the tenacity or cohesion of pure water is greater than that of soap and water is that the mingling of the soap and water interferes with the perfect mobility of the molecules and diminishes the attraction.

15. He further investigated the cohesion of liquids, measuring the tenacity of soap-water films by placing on them pellets of cotton until they burst. It was concluded that the attractive force of the molecules of water for those of water (several hundred pounds per square inch) is approximately equal to that of the molecules of ice for those of ice. He explained that oil spreads over water because "the attraction of water for water is greater than that of oil for oil, while the attraction of the molecules of oil for each other is less than the attraction of the same molecules for water." These experiments in molecular physics were pioneering.

16. Finally, in his letter to the Reverend Mr. Dod, Henry described at some length his contribution to science in "the origin of mechanical power and the nature of the vital force." He defined and classified mechanical power as opposed to "vitality." Mechanical power, he said, is that which is capable of overcoming resistance, or that which is employed to do work; vitality is that mysterious principle which determines the form and arranges the atoms of organized matter. This "doctrine," as he termed it, was first presented in December 1844 to the American Philosophical Society.

This, then, was the man who came down from Princeton to head the Smithsonian Institution, a man at the very peak of a brilliant scientific career, with many fundamental discoveries to his credit. And we must always admire Henry for the high regard in which he held pure scientific research. To expand the boundaries of knowledge he believed to be his special forte, and he left to perhaps less imaginative and more enterprising men the task of applying this new knowledge to the uses of mankind. He did not even take out patents on his discoveries that might have made him a fortune, and in some instances he failed to publish his studies promptly, with the result that he can not be given full credit for some of them; for example, honors for the discovery of electromagnetic induction he must share with his contemporary Michael Faraday, the great English physicist and chemist.[4] Henry's natural modesty in claiming priority deterred him. He was more interested in having the approval of his scientific equals than the applause of the public. He saw clearly the value of abstract science and was eloquent in its defense. "He who loves truth for its own sake," he wrote, "feels that its highest claims are lowered and its moral influence marred by being continually summoned to the bar of immediate and palpable utility."

Housing the Institution

ONE OF THE first jobs confronting the new Smithsonian Secretary was to supervise the construction of a suitable building to be the home of the Institution. Congress already, in the Act of Establishment, had placed on the Board of Regents the responsibility for the choice of a site [5] and the erection of the building. It should be con-

[4] Credit for the discovery of the electrical principle of self-induction is now generally conceded as belonging to Henry, and this was officially recognized by the International Congress of Electricians in 1893, when the name *henry* was given to the standard of inductive resistance.

[5] President Polk himself helped the Regents in the selection of the site, but the final decision apparently followed the recommendation of Regent William W. Seaton, mayor of Washington. Polk wrote in his diary: "At nine o'clock this morning [Wednesday, Sept. 9, 1846] . . . I rode out in my carriage to meet the regents of the Smithsonian Institute [sic] on the public grounds lying west of the Capitol and south of the President's House, with a view to locate the site of that institution. I met the regents on the ground, and spent nearly an hour with them on foot in examining the grounds. Opinions were freely expressed. The most elevated ground,

structed of "plain and durable materials and structure, without unnecessary ornament, and of sufficient size, and with suitable rooms or halls for the reception and arrangement, upon a liberal scale, of objects of natural history, including a geological and mineralogical cabinet; also, a chemical laboratory, a library, a gallery of art, and the necessary lecture rooms."

There was little delay in getting the building under way, and the cornerstone was laid on the first day of May 1847, with impressive ceremonies attended by a large procession that included President Polk and his Cabinet. Accounts of the occasion tell us that the same gavel was used as that employed by George Washington when he laid the first cornerstone of the United States Capitol. The location of the cornerstone is not stated, though the northeast corner of the original foundation would have been the customary place. Either by weathering off of the inscription or by subsequent landscaping and filling in around the building, this architectural detail has been lost to us. An address fitting to the occasion was made by the Chancellor of the Institution, Vice President George M. Dallas, in which he described the building-to-be. "Its exterior," he said, "will present a specimen of the style of architecture that prevailed some seven centuries ago, chiefly in Germany, Normandy, and southern Europe, which preceded the Gothic, and continues to recommend itself, for structures like this, to the most enlightened judgment. It is known as the Norman, or, more strictly speaking, the Lombard style. It harmonizes alike with the extent, the grave uses, and the massive strength of the edifice; it exacts a certain variety in the form of its parts; and

and, as I think, the most eligible site, lies between 12th and 14th Streets containing about 32 acres. . . . Most of the regents expressed a preference for this location. Mr. W. W. Seaton . . . earnestly urged that the location should be made west [obviously Polk meant to say east] of 12th street and between that street and the Capitol. This is a lower situation than that west of it, and in no sense, as it strikes me, so eligible." The actual location—"upon the center of Tenth Street"—was determined on March 20, 1847, by a resolution of the building committee.

it authorizes any additions that convenience may require, no matter how seemingly irregular they may be."

The building was the first of this Romanesque twelfth-century style ever to be erected in this country for non-ecclesiastical uses. The architect was James Renwick, Jr., of New York, who also designed Grace Church and St. Patrick's Cathedral in New York City. The stone for the building, a red-brown freestone, was quarried from the banks of the Chesapeake and Ohio Canal, near Seneca Creek, Maryland, and only 23 miles from the site. The length of the building from east to west measures 447 feet, and its greatest width is 160 feet. Its nine towers of various shapes range from 60 to 145 feet in height.

By April 1849, the east wing of the building was sufficiently completed for occupancy by the Secretary and his staff. Before the end of the year the west wing was finished. The entire building, interior and exterior, was not completed immediately, however, and some construction was still going on in 1857, although the main edifice seems to have been finished in December 1854.

On January 24, 1865, in spite of the fact that precautions had been taken to make the Smithsonian Building fireproof, a fire broke out in the main portion, destroying the roof, the interior of the upper story, the interior of the two large north towers, and the large south tower. Although the losses were not considered to be severe, many records, publications, and manuscripts were destroyed, as well as apparatus and a large stock of tools and instruments. Perhaps the most serious loss was the collection of the personal effects of James Smithson, including his numerous manuscripts. Almost completely destroyed, too, was a valuable series of Indian portraits and scenes (in all about 150 canvases) which had been temporarily deposited by the artist John Mix Stanley in 1852; only seven of these pictures were saved. The building was repaired at a cost of about $150,000.[6]

6 One account of the fire says: "A series of cases intended for ethnological specimens had been constructed in the gallery on the second floor,

Early Operation of the Smithsonian

BY THE TIME of the fire, the Institution had been in operation nearly twenty years. During this period Professor Henry had successfully put into effect a plan of organization which was thereafter to guide its course.

Even before he left Princeton, Henry had been requested by the Board of Regents to study the will of James Smithson and present a plan of organization. Thus when he arrived in Washington he had already given considerable thought to the problem of what the proper functions of the Institution should be. He laid down a few basic principles on which he thought the organization should operate. One was that the Institution should undertake nothing that could be done adequately by other agencies of the country. Another was that the Smithson bequest was intended for the benefit of mankind, and that, therefore, "all unnecessary expenditure on local objects would be a perversion of the trust." The United States Government would act as trustee to carry out the will of Smithson. The Institution, however, would not be a national establishment in the usual sense, but rather the establishment of an individual, to bear and perpetuate his name. The objectives of the Institution were clear—first, to increase, and second, to diffuse, knowledge among men. Inasmuch as the will did not define or restrict in any way the particular kind of knowledge to be diffused and augmented, no branch of knowledge could rightly be ex-

---

which made it necessary to rearrange the Indian paintings. The day was extremely cold, and with a view to their comfort in hanging the pictures the workmen brought a stove into the room and inadequately inserted the pipe in a ventilating flue which opened under the roof [i.e., in the wall between the studs next to the space containing the chimney flue]. The conflagration which ensued burnt out the entire upper story of the main building, as well as the central main towers on both the north and south sides. . . . The contents of the upper gallery were almost entirely destroyed. These . . . consisted mainly of the Indian paintings of J. M. Stanley, Charles B. King and others, probably other paintings, and the marble copy of the Dying Gladiator."

cluded from its share of attention. Said Henry, "Smithson was well aware that knowledge should not be viewed as existing in isolated parts, but as a whole, each portion of which throws light on all the other, and that the tendency of all is to improve the human mind, and to give it new sources of power and enjoyment."

With these liberal principles in mind, Henry proposed that the Institution, in order to *increase knowledge,* should (1) stimulate men of talent to make original researches, by offering suitable rewards for memoirs containing new truths, these memoirs to be published in a series of quarto volumes called "Smithsonian Contributions to Knowledge"; and (2) appropriate annually a portion of the income for particular researches, under the direction of suitable persons. To *diffuse knowledge* he proposed (1) to publish a series of periodical reports on the progress of the different branches of knowledge; and (2) to publish occasionally separate treatises on subjects of general interest. At the meeting of the Board of Regents on December 8, 1847, Henry presented the details of this general plan for the Board's consideration and approval. Furthermore, the plan was submitted to a number of literary and scientific societies, and it must have been gratifying to the new secretary to have his work widely approved. "In every case," he reported, the program "received their unqualified approbation." On December 13 the plan was officially adopted. The stage was set and the work of the Smithsonian Institution could begin.

As a matter of fact, it had already started. In May 1847, Professor Henry had received a letter from two archeologists of Chillicothe, Ohio—E. George Squier, A.M., and E. H. Davis, M.D.—who had been investigating the ancient Mound Builders of the Mississippi Valley region. They had prepared an elaborate manuscript based on a study of over two hundred of the Indian mounds, comprising, they said, the results of extensive original surveys and explorations, and they wished to submit it for publication by the Smithsonian Institution. This, it appeared, promised to be what Henry was looking for to initiate the "Smithsonian Contributions to Knowledge." He received the manuscript and, after submitting it for critical examination to several competent scholars, accepted it for publication. It was published on December 1, 1848, under the title *Ancient Monuments of the Mississippi Valley,* illustrated by 48 lithograph plates and 207 wood engravings. Uncopyrighted, a copy was sent to every principal library of the world, though the edition was small. It was the first scientific publication to be issued by the Institution, as well as a pioneer work in American archeology.

It should be remembered that in 1848 there were very few outlets for the publication of such monographs as that by Squier and Davis. True, the American Philosophical Society at Philadelphia and the American Academy of Arts and Sciences at Boston issued publications, and an increasing number of scientific journals were springing up, many of them organs of scientific societies. But for the most part authors had to pay for the publication of their work, especially if it was anything as pretentious and costly as *Ancient Monuments of the Mississippi Valley.* Learned societies then did not have much money to spend on quarto volumes and expensive illustrations. It can be readily appreciated what this new Smithsonian publication plan meant to the scientists of America. They now had a new and dignified medium for the publication of their researches and could be assured of world-wide distribution of their papers. Henry knew, though he had himself been dilatory in the prompt publication of some of his own electromagnetic discoveries, that science is valueless unless given to the world to be put to whatever use the human race desires or is capable of. Said Henry, "The real workingmen in the line of original research hail this part of the plan as a new era in the history of American science."

The "Contributions" soon became widely known

PLATE 8.   View of downtown Washington about the time of the Civil
War, the Smithsonian Building showing at left. At right, construction work
is in progress on part of the United States Treasury Building

PLATE 9.   Earliest known photograph of the Smithsonian Building, 1866

PLATE 10. Meeting of the National Academy of Sciences in Mineral Hall, Smithsonian Institution, about 1871. Those identified are as follows: 1, Joseph Henry, presiding; 2, Mary Henry; 3, W. J. Rhees; 4, Frank Wigglesworth Clarke; 5, J. S. Newberry; 6, J. C. Dalton; 7, J. E. Hilgard; 8, J. J. Woodward; 9, Peter Parker; 10, Alfred M. Mayer; 11, William Ferrel; 12, Benjamin Silliman; 13, C. E. Dutton; 14, Emil Bessels; 15, Arnold Guyot; 16, J. H. C. Coffin; 17, B. A. Gould; 18, Elias Loomis; 19, C. A. Schott; 20, George Engelmann; 22, Simon Newcomb; 23, Lewis Henry Morgan; 24, A. A. Michelson; 25, J. S. Billings; 26, S. Wier Mitchell; 27, F. M. Endlich

among scholars, and in the ensuing years many important monographs appeared in the series. The only requirement was that each paper should constitute a positive addition to knowledge based on original research. The series ran for sixty-eight years, being discontinued in 1916. A few of the well-known papers in this series include: "Ancient Monuments of the Mississippi Valley," already mentioned; "Memoir on Mechanical Flight," by Langley and Manly; Coffin's "The Winds of the Globe"; Shaler's "Comparison of Earth and Moon"; Morley's "On the Densities of Oxygen and Hydrogen, and the Ratio of their Atomic Weights"; and Morgan's "Systems of Consanguinity and Affinity of the Human Family."

The reaction of the general public toward the Smithsonian was both favorable and unfavorable, but Secretary Henry believed that those who opposed its policies did not understand what the Institution was trying to do and that they should be informed. Above all, he took a firm stand that the promotion of original research should be the backbone of its plan of operation. In his 1852 Report he said, "The proposition is frequently urged upon the Regents, by persons who have not duly considered the will of Smithson, or who fail to appreciate the importance of the present plan, that a large portion of the income should be devoted to the diffusion of a knowledge of some popular branch of practical art; and there may be some fear that a timid policy on the part of the friends of the Institution will lead them to favor such a plan." Three years later he wrote, "From the number of letters received during the past year, containing spontaneous expression of opinion relative to the course pursued by the Regents, there can be no doubt that the policy which has been adopted is the one most in accordance with the views of the intelligent part of the community." He believed in educating the public to his views. "The Regents will, doubtless," he said, "adhere to the line of policy which has been adopted; turn neither to the right nor to the left to catch an apparently favorable breath of public applause, and continue to *lead,* rather than *follow,* public opinion." And it is to be noted that as many as 20,000 copies of some of his early reports were printed by Congress for distribution. Gradually the soundness of his plan became established, and "by its means," wrote Henry, "a reputation has been established and an influence exerted in the line of the promotion of knowledge as wide as the civilized world."

The Smithsonian Library and Museum

THE ORIGINAL ACT of Congress establishing the Smithsonian made specific provision for a library, and it was, therefore, incumbent upon the new Secretary to begin its formation at once. On January 26, 1847, Charles Coffin Jewett, a young professor of modern languages and literature at Brown University, was appointed Assistant Secretary of the Institution to serve as librarian. The initial purpose of the library was to procure "a complete collection of the memoirs and transactions of learned societies throughout the world and an entire series of the most important scientific and literary periodicals," and it was agreed that a special library of this kind could be a means of both increasing and diffusing knowledge. Professor Jewett was an energetic man with ideas and was far in advance of his time in library planning and technique. He became recognized as one of the most active librarians and bibliographers of his day, and under his direction the Smithsonian collection grew, in six years, to 32,000 volumes. It was fast becoming, under his tutelage, a national reference and bibliographic center. One of Jewett's original ideas was a plan whereby, instead of the expensive printing of catalogues of American libraries, separate stereotyped titles would be made available to librarians. In this way a general catalogue of the public libraries of the United States could be constructed. This was a genuine contribution to library science and was later taken up by the Library of Congress.

Jewett performed fine work in laying the foundation for the Smithsonian Library. If anything, however, he was over-ambitious in plans for the future, in view of the Institution's limited funds, which had to be spread over an increasing variety of activities. Jewett felt that he should spend on the library all that the law allowed. In 1855 a difference of opinion arose between Henry and Jewett over the library administration and authority, chiefly concerning expenditures and the nature of the library—whether it should be developed along predominantly scientific or literary lines. Science and Henry prevailed, and Professor Jewett was retired from office after eight years' service. He became Superintendent of the Boston Public Library, where he rendered notable service for a number of years.

This library question, to be sure, was an animated one; Jewett's release started a Congressional investigation and caused the resignation of the Honorable Rufus Choate from the Board of Regents. In general, however, Secretary Henry's policy was upheld, namely, that the library should not be developed at the expense of the other activities of the organization. The indorsement of the Secretary's policy by Congress definitely answered the question as to whether the creation of a great library should be one of the Institution's main objects. Henry felt strongly that the Smithsonian should not engage in any way in competition with other organizations, and that, although a modest library of scientific literature was needed for the use of its own staff, it was not the function of the Smithsonian to build up a large national library in competition with the Library of Congress and other institutions. Rather, let the Smithsonian Library work in cooperation with other libraries, but avoid needless duplication of functions and materials.

An example of this duplication was the matter of copyright. For nearly thirteen years after the founding of the Institution, the law required anyone wishing to secure copyright of a book to deposit one copy with the librarian

45

of the Smithsonian Institution and another copy with the librarian of Congress. This dual requirement, it seemed to Henry, was unnecessary and promised to be a burdensome one; and in 1857 he succeeded in having section 10 of the original Smithsonian Act of 1846 repealed, and the Library of Congress became the sole copyright depository.

A few years later, in 1866, another "merger" was effected, when the Smithsonian Library by Congressional authority turned over to the Library of Congress about 40,000 volumes of scientific works, to form the basis of what has since been known as the "Smithsonian Deposit." "The object of this transfer," wrote Henry, "is not, of course, to separate this unique and highly prized collection of books from its relations to the Smithsonian Institution, for it must still bear its name and be subject to its control, but merely to deposit it where its preservation will be more certain [thinking probably of the fire in the Smithsonian Building] and its usefulness more extended." In the eighty-odd years that have passed since the original "Smithsonian Deposit," almost a million volumes and parts have been added to it, to make it one of the largest collections of scientific literature in the world. It is especially complete in the transactions and proceedings of scientific societies.

The removal of these books not only relieved the space problem in the Smithsonian Building but also eased the financial strain by putting upon the shoulders of Congress the responsibility for the upkeep of this collection. Furthermore, it was in harmony with Joseph Henry's general policy of trying to keep the organization of the Institution from becoming too cumbersome and from outgrowing its income. Besides a library, the Smithsonian Act had directed that a museum and an art gallery should be provided for under the Smithsonian Institution. Henry, however, though he was not openly opposed to these, believed that they should be projects only temporarily undertaken by the Institution, to be turned over to other agencies when possible. In this way, he felt, the Smithsonian could concentrate its activities on matters of benefit to all mankind rather than on those of local and restricted interest.

The museum was to remain under the direction of the Smithsonian and to grow into a large and important organization supported by Government funds. Like the library, it flourished inordinately, until in 1866 the collections, "taken as a whole, constitute the largest and best series of minerals, fossils, rocks, animals, and plants of the entire continent of North America, in the world." Of the large North American and European mammals it had the best collection in the United States; of birds, its collection ranked second only to that of the Academy of Natural Sciences of Philadelphia; and of fishes only Louis Agassiz had a larger collection. So even though Secretary Henry would have preferred the museum subordinated or even divorced from the Institution, Congress ruled otherwise, and it continued to develop and occupy generous quarters in the new building. On July 5, 1850, Spencer Fullerton Baird, biologist, was made Assistant Secretary of the Institution to take charge of the museum and to aid in the publication program. Baird as Assistant Secretary, and later as Secretary, was to play a signal role in the development of the museum and in the affairs of the Institution.

Smithsonian Cooperation—Pioneering in Meteorology

ANOTHER of Joseph Henry's principles which guided the Smithsonian's course of action from the very beginning was cooperation. He early realized that if the Institution were to fulfill its high purposes it must extend its activities and influence beyond that directly covered by its limited income. To do this meant to fit into the scientific life of America in the give-and-take spirit. It was well enough to spend large sums in aid of research and in publishing and distributing "Contributions to Knowledge" by scientific investigators who had no other channel by which to make known the results of their researches, but it was necessary also for other institutions and individuals, in turn, to contribute to the work of the Smithsonian. Something of this kind was absolutely necessary, for the Smithsonian simply did not have the funds or the staff to carry on all the activities it was called upon to perform. In return it would lend its prestige, publish results, and correlate.

In his second annual Report (for the year 1848) Henry outlined a project that was to furnish a notable example of this cooperation. It was an experiment in the science of meteorology. His plan was to obtain weather reports from a great network of voluntary observers scattered over the country. He was especially interested in assembling long-range data on climate and weather from stations in every region, and in this way to furnish a sound foundation upon which the science of meteorology could build. We know today how far this science has advanced, how much we depend on weather forecasts and the daily weather report. We remember what an important part meteorology played in World War II. But in Henry's day it was new; Henry was a pioneer, and he and the Smithsonian must have credit for initiating a part of the work that finally culminated in the United States Weather Bureau.

After persuading the Regents of the Institution to support his project, he went ahead. There would be, he said, three classes of observers: "One class, without instruments, to observe the face of the sky as to its clearness, the extent of cloud, the direction and force of wind, the beginning and end of rain, snow, etc. A second class, furnished with thermometers, who besides making the observations above mentioned, will record variations of temperature. The third class, furnished with full sets of instruments, to observe all the elements at present deemed important in the science of meteorology."

This proved to be a cooperative enterprise of the highest degree. First were the individual voluntary observers distributed over the entire continent, and by 1852 these numbered about two hundred, reporting directly to the

Smithsonian. Then the states of New York and Massachusetts cooperated by setting up weather stations with instruments at various academies; these had state support but were directed by the Institution. Further observations were made at a hundred or so military posts of the United States, under the direction of the Surgeon General of the Army. Separate series of observations were made by exploring and surveying parties and reported back to the Institution. In Canada, or British America as it was then called, observations were made at various posts of the Hudson's Bay Company. Stations reached to Nova Scotia, Panama, and Bermuda, and there was one observer at Ascención, Paraguay. The work had the active support of such leading meteorologists as Arnold Guyot, James P. Espy, Elias Loomis, James H. Coffin, and William Ferrel. Professor Guyot, the Swiss scientist who had just come to the United States, was entrusted with selecting and ordering the improved instruments required, and with the job of preparing a set of "Directions for Meteorological Observations" to serve as a guide for the observers.

Another paragraph in Henry's second annual Report was epoch-making. "As a part of the system of meteorology," he said, "it is proposed to employ, as far as our funds permit, the magnetic telegraph in the investigation of atmospheric phenomena. By this means, not only notice of the approach of a storm may be given to distant observers, but also attention may be directed to particular phenomena, which can only be properly studied by the simultaneous observations of persons widely separated from each other. For example, the several phases presented by a thunderstorm, or by the aurora borealis, may be telegraphed to a distance, and the synchronous appearances compared and recorded in stations far removed from each other. Also, by the same means, a single observatory . . . may give notice to all persons along the telegraph lines, of the occurrence of interesting phenomena. . . ." Knowledge of an approaching storm, he thought, could be of great advantage to agriculture and commerce, and this, he concluded, "is a subject deserving the attention of the general government."

Henry, then, must be given credit for first utilizing the electric telegraph in this way, although it may have been suggested by others. As the American meteorologist Cleveland Abbe wrote in 1871 in the *American Journal of Science,* "The Smithsonian Institution first in the world organized a comprehensive system of telegraphic meteorology." By 1857, a series of weather reports was coming in via the National Telegraph line from New Orleans to New York and as far west as Cincinnati; these reports were first published in the *Washington Evening Star.* Naturally they excited much interest and were soon extended farther north and westward. The next year a daily weather map, compiled from telegraphic reports received at 10 o'clock every morning, was exhibited in the Smithsonian Building.

All this combined in a practical way the telegraph and the work of the weather observers throughout the country. The fast-accumulating weather data were soon put, however, to strictly scientific uses. Voluminous reports, maps, tables, and charts were prepared and published on all phases of the work—rainfall, snowfall, temperatures, barometric pressure, storms, meteors, auroras, etc. Between 1852 and 1884 four editions of *A Collection of Meteorological Tables* (later expanded into the "Smithsonian Meteorological Tables"), compiled by Professor Guyot, were issued; and there were many more important scientific fruits of the work. Although the Civil War, and also the disastrous Smithsonian fire, interrupted the work in many ways, it did not end the cooperative spirit that the enterprise seemed to engender. In 1864 the North American Telegraphic Association, covering the entire United States and Canada, contributed the free use of all its lines for the scientific objects of the Institution. In the meantime, however, agitation began for "a meteorological department under one comprehensive system with an adequate appropriation of funds." Henry, too, favored such a plan, and in 1869 Congress passed a resolution establishing the Weather Bureau of the United States Signal Service. Consequently, the Smithsonian's system of meteorological reports was turned over to the new bureau. Few new agencies of the Federal Government have ever had so generous a birthright and so solid a foundation. It represents perhaps the greatest experiment in cooperation that the Smithsonian ever attempted, but its unqualified success was an inspiration and pattern for many less pretentious undertakings.

The International Exchange Service

ALWAYS UPPERMOST in Joseph Henry's mind was the purpose that James Smithson prescribed for his Institution —the "increase and diffusion of knowledge among men." This, its primary function, became the Institution's motto.[7] "The worth and importance of the Institution," wrote Henry in 1852, "are not to be estimated by what it accumulates within the walls of its building, but by what it sends forth to the world."

Henry referred not only to the distribution of the Institution's own publications but also to another effective means of diffusing knowledge which since 1849 had facilitated the distribution and exchange of literary and scientific publications between this and other countries. Even today after a hundred years it is still one of the functions of the Smithsonian, although the financial support of the Exchange Service has long since (1881) been shouldered by Congressional appropriations. Henry left much of the organization of the Exchange Service to Assistant Secretary Baird and put him in charge of its administration.

With the appearance in 1848 of its first publication, *Ancient Monuments of the Mississippi Valley,* the Institution was confronted with a problem of how best to dis-

---

[7] The seal of the Smithsonian Institution adopted in 1847 carried a left-facing likeness of the founder, James Smithson. The new seal, designed by Augustus St. Gaudens and adopted in 1893, carries the words "For the increase and diffusion of knowledge among men—*per orbem.*"

tribute copies where they would be the most useful and accessible. In addition to the American distribution, a few hundred copies were sent to scientific and other learned institutions abroad with the request that they exchange publications. At first the number of responses to the proposal was small, but by 1852 Professor Henry reported that 4,744 articles had been received. To continue this desirable exchange of intelligence with other nations, Henry appointed agents in a number of foreign countries. The Royal Society of London was especially cooperative. Gradually the system expanded until Henry was able to offer to other learned societies of the United States the facilities set up at the Institution for distributing their publications abroad. The Exchange Service became a clearing house for the receipt and distribution of scientific literature. Incoming packages of exchange publications were admitted free of duty and were allowed to pass the customs without the delay of an examination. Many of the great transportation companies and steamship lines extended to the Exchange Service the privilege of free freight.

From the beginning the United States Government departments made use of the Exchange Service in obtaining official documents of other governments in exchange for their own. In 1867 Congress passed an act systematizing this governmental interchange, but it was not until 1881 that any Congressional financial support was given the system. By that time the Exchange Service was costing so much, in spite of generous free freight and other concessions, that something had to be done, and Congress assumed part of its support by appropriating $3,000. This support was continued and increased, until just before World War II the annual appropriation for the Service reached approximately $50,000.

For about forty years the International Exchanges operated unofficially, so to speak, from the standpoint of international law. Beginning in 1875 international conferences held in Paris and Brussels discussed the exchange between countries not only of governmental documents but also of scientific and literary publications, and in 1886 a formal agreement was reached. Eight nations ratified the convention—"International Exchange of Official Documents, Scientific and Literary Publications"—and it was officially proclaimed by the President of the United States on January 15, 1889. Other nations accepted the convention later, and with those countries that did not ratify special arrangements were made for exchanges. The Smithsonian Institution was recognized as the official exchange agency of the United States.

The Exchange System in operation at the present time functions with slight modification from that inaugurated by Henry. Libraries, scientific societies, educational institutions, and individuals in this country who wish to distribute their publications abroad as gifts or exchanges send the separate addressed packages to the Smithsonian Institution, carriage cost prepaid. There they are sorted by countries and forwarded with similar shipments from other organizations to the exchange agencies in other parts of the world, where they are distributed to the addressees. Similarly, shipments of publications from exchange agencies abroad to the Smithsonian are distributed free to addressees in the United States.

The Smithsonian International Exchange Service has now been in operation for a full century, with but two major interruptions, these occasioned by World Wars I and II. Even throughout the years of World War II exchanges were continued with all countries of the Western Hemisphere and with a few in other parts of the world. The Exchange Service has demonstrated itself as a very tangible expression of the Smithsonian Institution's part in "the diffusion of knowledge." It, again, is an instance of that cooperative kind of enterprise envisioned by Joseph Henry as the most effective means for the Smithsonian to fulfill its purpose.

Smithsonian Lectures

STILL ANOTHER MEANS of "diffusing knowledge," especially among the residents of the National Capital, was
initiated as soon as the new Smithsonian Building became
available. This was a series of free lectures. Professor
Henry never fully favored these lectures, for he felt that,
being local, they were "too limited in their influence to
meet a proper interpretation of the will of Smithson."
However, they had been ordered by Congress, and Henry
could not do otherwise than to provide them. He sought
to maintain the lectures on a high plane, "to improve the
public taste rather than to elicit popular applause." The
lecturers, many of whom were invited from a distance,
were paid for their services in accordance with the modest
appropriations made for the purpose, but it is evident in
noting some of their names that Professor Henry was able
to obtain the best to be had.

It was—the mid-nineteenth century—the era of the
popular lecture. Long before the radio, motion picture,
and other modern forms of mass entertainment, the average man seemed hungry for knowledge and willing to put
forth effort to improve his education; a series of a dozen
lectures on geology, astronomy, history, or literature was
enthusiastically welcomed. Every city of any size had its
lecture courses (this was before the days of the Chau-
tauqua when every village also had them), usually sponsored by intellectual associations, such as the Lowell
Institute of Boston, the Athenaeum of Richmond, and
the Cooper Union of New York; and in many cases the
lecturer's remuneration was liberal enough to attract men
of reputation. The great Emerson traveled a Lyceum circuit that took him as far west as St. Louis and Milwaukee.
Dr. Oliver Wendell Holmes went to Cincinnati and Louisville. "Public lectures," wrote Henry in the Report for
1852, "have become one of the characteristics of the
day, and next to the press tend, more than any other

means of diffusing knowledge, to impress the public mind."

The Smithsonian lectures were given chiefly while Congress was in session. The first lectures under the auspices of the Institution were a series delivered, beginning on February 25, 1847, in Washington's Odd Fellows Hall, by William Scoresby, the English Arctic explorer, on "The Construction and Use of the Rosse Telescope." Next came four on "Modern Athens," delivered by Prof. Adolphus Louis Koeppen of Denmark in Carusi's Hall, beginning on April 6, 1849. A course of six on "Geology" followed, beginning on April 30, 1849, by Dr. Edward Hitchcock, president of Amherst College—the first to be given in the Smithsonian Building. As facilities improved the program was expanded; in 1850, during the last session of Congress, lecturers appeared and delivered one to several lectures apiece, ranging from a single lecture on "Holland," by the Reverend Dr. George W. Bethune, to a course on "The Unity of the Plan of the Animal Creation," by Prof. Louis Agassiz, of Cambridge, Mass. "Whatever may have been the effect of these lectures in the way of diffusing knowledge," commented Henry, "it is evident, from the character of the men by whom they were delivered, that they presented truths intended to elevate and improve the moral and intellectual condition of the hearers." In the roster of lecturers for the next few years we find such names as Dr. Benjamin Silliman, of Yale College; Prof. Benjamin Silliman, Jr., of Yale; President Mark Hopkins, of Williams College; Dr. B. A. Gould, Jr., of Cambridge; Prof. Louis Agassiz, who in 1863 became a Regent of the Institution; Prof. Stephen Alexander, of the College of New Jersey; Prof. A. Guyot; and the Honorable Henry Barnard, educational reformer.

As the years went by, however, the popularity of the lectures began to wane somewhat, no doubt aided by Henry's reservations as to the Smithsonian's proper interest in such lectures, valuable as they might be. Today, except for an occasional one, usually by a member of the staff, and the annual Arthur Lecture on some phase of solar research, the "Smithsonian lecture" is but a memory. In late years the lingering lecture needs of the general populace of the City of Washington seem to have been supplied chiefly by the National Geographic Society in its popular winter series. The lecture was an influential phase of American life that is largely past, and it is probable that modern educational and entertainment methods have permanently supplanted it. But it was good while it lasted, and the Smithsonian played an active and dignified part in the half century or so of its greatest popularity. The Lecture Room in the Smithsonian Building was entirely burned out by the fire of 1865, and it was never reconstructed as such.

The Secretary's Extra-Curricular Activities

PROFESSOR HENRY'S OWN RESEARCHES during this period suffered because of his administrative duties, but by no means did his scientific work entirely cease, and his contributions to science at Washington were numerous. He actively supported the American Association for the Advancement of Science, which in 1848 he had helped to organize. During the Civil War he was a trusted friend of President Lincoln and was called upon many times for advice in scientific matters. He assisted Lincoln in planning the National Academy of Sciences and was one of its original members. Significant, too, was the interest Henry took in the 1861 balloon experiments of the pioneer aeronaut Thaddeus S. C. Lowe, chief of the aeronautical corps during the Civil War. He encouraged Lowe in his tests and helped him gain an audience with President Lincoln, which resulted in the use of balloons in the Civil War. In 1864 Henry wrote, "A large share of my time has been devoted for the last four years to investigations required by the public exigencies." This part played by Henry and the Institution in the Civil War and the services he rendered to the various Executive Departments in scientific matters can never fully be told, however, as the official records and correspondence were lost in the fire. During the War he was a member of a commission "to examine and report upon various investigations and experiments intended to facilitate the operations of the war and to improve the art of navigation." "Many of the experiments," G. Brown Goode records, "were conducted at the Institution. From the top of the great tower, night after night, lights were flashed to distant stations, in connection with tests of methods of signaling; and many a time Professor Henry's companion in these studies was President Lincoln, glad to leave the scene of turmoil in which his days were passed and to seek rest and inspiration in the quiet companionship of such a man as Henry."

While serving on the United States Lighthouse Board, of which he was made chairman in 1871, Henry conducted a series of experiments that led to the substitution of lard oil for sperm oil for use in the extensive system of lighthouse beacons, before kerosene became an abundant fuel. This, it has been estimated, saved the Government as much as $100,000 a year. Based on his studies of the laws of sound, he also devised a siren fog-signaling system, which was later adopted by the Government.

In 1854 he experimented on the strength of different kinds of building stones offered for the extension of the United States Capitol, and conducted research in the field of acoustics. He constructed a large sulphuric-acid barometer, which was in successful use for many years, and had its readings constantly recorded. Other important studies of Henry's might be mentioned to show the variety of his interests and abilities. Yet he was so scrupulous that he allowed none of his own researches to be published by the Institution. One account states, "Many of his most valuable papers must be searched for in unsuggestive volumes of Agricultural or Lighthouse Board Reports."

Busy as he was with Smithsonian affairs, he somehow found time for all these activities. He was called upon to make many public addresses, and his position required that he keep in close contact with scientific men and work throughout the country. In 1868 he was chosen President of the National Academy of Sciences and held that position until his death. Meetings of the Academy were held in the Smithsonian Building. In 1871 he was active in organizing the Philosophical Society of Washington and served as its president as long as he lived. In 1870 the Board of Regents granted him a leave of absence (plus expenses) that he might take a trip to Europe "for the interests of the Institution in the promotion of science . . . and to consult with savants and societies of Great Britain and the continent." This trip was most profitable for Henry. Among other activities, he testified before an English Government Scientific Commission regarding the methods and aims of the Institution. After an absence of four and a half months he returned, much improved in health and with impressions concerning science and education in the old World that were to prove of value to him in directing the affairs of the Institution.

Visitors to the Smithsonian today are sometimes told that in the early days some members of the staff resided in the Smithsonian Building. Professor Henry and his family lived in the east wing for twenty-three years—from 1855 until his death. The Henrys were a family of the old school, close-knit, loyal, and devoted to one another, deriving their greatest pleasure in each other's company. There were four children—the three daughters, Mary, Caroline, and Helen, and the son, William Alexander Henry, who died in 1862 in early manhood. Two others had died in infancy. The family's residence in the Smithsonian Building spanned the entire period of the Civil War. From it they watched the Confederate flag flying over Alexandria six miles away; saw the regiments passing through the city; followed the daily news of battles; looked upon prisoners and wounded being brought in; waited for news of peace; lived anxiously through Lincoln's assassination; wondered, even with the Union saved, what was to happen to the nation. Through it all their home was a bright spot, more than a home to the

PLATE 11.   Spencer Fullerton Baird, second secretary
of the Smithsonian Institution, 1878-1887

PLATE 12. The first National Museum Building under construction, 1879. From left to right: General M. C. Meigs, U.S.A.; General William T. Sherman, Regent and Chairman of Building Committee; Peter Parker, Regent; Spencer F. Baird, Secretary, Smithsonian Institution; Adolf Cluss, Architect; W. J. Rhees, Smithsonian Chief Clerk; Daniel Leech, Correspondence Clerk

PLATE 13. John Wesley Powell (1834-1902), explorer of the Colorado River, Director of the U. S. Geological Survey, founder and First Chief of the Bureau of American Ethnology

PLATE 14.
George Brown Goode as
a young man at Wesleyan
University

PLATE 15.
George Brown Goode as
Assistant Secretary of the
Smithsonian Institution

Henrys. It was a center of intellectual life in Washington; and always welcome were visiting scientists, professors, writers, lecturers, officers, and other distinguished visitors to the city. Some of the cheerful fireplaces of the Henrys' living quarters are still in use in the east-wing executive offices in the Smithsonian Building—impressing one now as a rather refreshing anachronism among the modern Government office buildings on Washington's Mall.

Joseph Henry had been reared in the stern atmosphere of Scotch Presbyterianism. He was a practicing Christian and brought up his family accordingly. His science never destroyed his religious faith, nor did he ever see any basic conflict between science and religion. Like Lincoln, the family attended the New York Avenue Presbyterian Church, and they were active in its affairs.

In December 1877 Henry was stricken with nephritis and died the following May 13, in his eighty-first year. In his death American science lost its most distinguished leader and the Smithsonian Institution its great "architect" and chief. He was buried in Oak Hill Cemetery in Georgetown, D. C. Tributes and eulogies were paid him by statesmen and scientists, memorial services were held in the United States Capitol, and a bronze statue was erected to his memory on the grounds of the Smithsonian.

John Quincy Adams said of the Smithsonian, "Of all the foundations or establishments for pious or charitable uses which ever signalized the spirit of the age or the comprehensive beneficence of the founder, none can be named more deserving the approbation of mankind." Joseph Henry, more than any other person, made that statement true, and that is his eternal monument. On May 17, 1878, four days after Henry's death, Assistant Secretary Spencer Fullerton Baird, of Carlisle, Pa., was elected the new Secretary.

5

BAIRD AND THE
NATIONAL MUSEUM

SPENCER FULLERTON BAIRD, Henry's successor, has been called the "father of the National Museum," a title well deserved. It is true that from its very beginning the Smithsonian was charged with the responsibility of maintaining a museum, but it was Baird, not Henry, who gave it his unqualified blessing. Baird was the consummate museum man—a great naturalist, an untiring collector of specimens, a wise and skillful organizer, a hard worker, and a self-sacrificing and lovable personality. There was little doubt, with these qualifications and twenty-eight years of experience as Henry's Assistant Secretary, that he was the right man to carry on the work of the beloved physicist who preceded him. It was fitting, too, that a biologist should succeed a physicist, to guard against the Institution's following too closely and for too long a time the particular interests and proclivities of its head. There have now (1948) been six Secretaries, and this tradition has been maintained, with the physical and the natural sciences equally represented and alternating.

Early Years

BAIRD was born on February 23, 1823, in Reading, Pa., son of Samuel and Lydia Baird. His father, a lawyer and "man of fine culture," died when Spencer was only ten years old, and the family soon thereafter moved to Carlisle, Pa., in the Cumberland Valley. At Carlisle was located Dickinson College, a school which at that time had been in existence (with its ups and downs) for half a century and was under the direction of the Methodist Episcopal Church. It was a small college, maintaining strict discipline, but, as Baird's biographer W. H. Dall has said, "the long series of illustrious names which grace the catalogue of this ancient seat of learning shows that the discipline and paternal care of its Faculty were far from being wasted." Dickinson College turned out students of a serious type, and the Baird boys, William and Spencer, were among them. Spencer was graduated in 1840, at the age of seventeen.

By this time his interest in natural history had already become well rooted. With his brother William he roamed the countryside around Carlisle and collected many birds, mammals, plants, fossils, and other natural-history objects. When, ten years later, he was called to Washington, he took most of these collections of fauna and flora with him, and they are still preserved in their various departments at the National Museum. Even before his graduation he spent long hours studying such works as Alexander Wilson's *American Ornithology* and François André Michaux's *North American Sylva,* and he had already begun to correspond with John James Audubon, the artist-birdman. Audubon was quick to recognize the potentialities of his young friend and asked Baird to collect small mammals for him, as he was then working on his *Quadrupeds of North America.* "Your style and the descriptions you have sent me," wrote Audubon, "prove to me that an old head may from time to time be found on young shoulders!" On a trip to Philadelphia in September 1839, Baird had seen Audubon's great folio on American birds, and one can imagine the thrill this must have given him and the pride he must have had in Audubon's friendship and trust.

After graduation he continued his private studies and began to read in medicine, and in the fall of 1841 decided to go to New York to study medicine. The following January he returned home to recover from a serious illness and was never to finish his medical course, although the Philadelphia Medical College, in 1848, conferred upon him an honorary M. D. degree. A stronger urge—natural history—was pulling him, and he did not try to escape.

In New York he had met Audubon, whom he found "very unlike my preconceived idea of him," and had occasion to meet other leading naturalists of the day—George Newbold Lawrence, the ornithologist; Titian Ramsay Peale, the artist; John Torrey, the botanist; and others.

Back in Carlisle he studied assiduously, making use of all the library facilities available. He made long collecting excursions by foot, building up his "cabinet of natural history." He went occasionally to Philadelphia where he met such eminent scientists as John Cassin. He began an active correspondence with naturalists in many cities, exchanging ideas and specimens and making lasting friendships that were to stand him in excellent stead in later years. His brother William had procured a job in the Treasury Department at the National Capital, and the two kept up an active correspondence. Spencer's letters especially were full of natural-history observations and data of all sorts. In July 1842 Spencer visited his brother in Washington, took great interest in the libraries, public buildings, and the museum of the Patent Office, and made new friends. He hoped that he might get a position in the Patent Office Museum as curator, but this did not materialize, and he returned to Carlisle early in September.

The next year was a signal one for the young naturalist, for it marked the appearance of his first scientific paper. It was a technical bird study entitled "Descriptions of Two Species, Supposed to be New, of the Genus *Tyrannula* Swainson, Found in Cumberland County, Pennsylvania"; it bore the names of Spencer F. and William M. Baird as coauthors and was published in Volume I of the *Proceedings* of the Academy of Natural Sciences of Philadelphia. Spencer's first "solo flight" in scientific publication, on the subject of "blue-print" photography in which he had been experimenting, was a paper published in December 1844 in the *Literary Record and Journal* of the Linnaean Association of Pennsylvania College; entitled "On the Application of Bi-chromate of Potassa to Photographic Purposes," it described the process of copying other flat objects on paper sensitized by bichromate of potassium.

He was beginning to be recognized in the scientific world. Both the Academy of Natural Sciences of Philadelphia and the Boston Society of Natural History elected him to corresponding membership. And he was still only twenty-one years of age. He continued his energetic correspondence, his travels, and his studies. At Commencement time in 1845 he was elected Honorary Professor of Natural History and Curator of the Cabinet of Dickinson College. "No salary and nothing to do," he commented. But this was another steppingstone, for a year later he was made full Professor of Natural History, at a beginning salary of $400 a year.

This was not much on which to support a wife (on August 8, 1846, Baird was married to Mary Helen Churchill of Carlisle), and it behooved him to be on the lookout for a better position. In January 1847 he received a letter from James Dwight Dana, Yale's distinguished zoologist and geologist, saying that he thought Baird "would make a good curator for the Smithsonian Institution" and that he would recommend him. The salary, Dana understood, was $1,500 with house rent. Baird acted at once and wrote not only to Secretary Joseph Henry but to others who might have influence and who might help him get the job. Testimonials came from Dana, Cassin, Audubon, Dr. Samuel G. Morton, and others, but the appointment evidently was not ready to be made. In the meantime, Baird continued his teaching and added to his correspondents Louis Agassiz, who had just come to Harvard College. He kept in touch with Professor Henry and with developments at the Smithsonian, and in July 1848, on a collecting tour that took him as far west as Cleveland, he visited Washington, met Secretary Henry, and obtained a small Smithsonian grant to aid in preparing illustrations for some of his researches. The following March he went to Washington again and had long conferences with Henry. The next year Henry granted him another small sum to aid his collecting work, and it is apparent that Baird was identifying himself more and more with the Smithsonian and looking toward the prospects of its future museum.

Secretary Henry desperately needed assistance, and Baird definitely was his choice, but lack of funds delayed the appointment until 1850. By April the matter was practically assured and Henry wrote Baird, "I shall expect of you not only assistance in the way of taking charge of the collections in Natural History, but also in publications—the correspondence and other business." On July 5 the Smithsonian Board of Regents met and elected Baird Assistant Secretary of the Institution, at a salary of $1,500. In November he bid farewell to Carlisle and with his wife and young daughter Lucy set out for Washington.

The National Museum

WE MUST LOOK now into the beginnings of the National Museum, which Baird had so large a part in developing, but whose genesis antedated the establishment of the

Smithsonian. Before 1800 public museums were almost nonexistent in the entire country, although private citizens here and there had built up collections, or "cabinets," of "curiosities." The first public museum in the United States was the Philadelphia Museum, founded in 1785 by the portrait-painter Charles Willson Peale. It was known as Peale's Museum and contained a vast array of popular attractions. About thirty years later, his son, Rembrandt Peale, established a museum and art gallery in Baltimore; and about the same time other American cities—Boston, Cincinnati, New York—began to boast of their museums, which if they did not rival those of the Old World were at least a good beginning. In Washington apparently there was no "official" museum except, perhaps, the Patent Office. In the Patent Office Building there had accumulated a collection of models of inventions that was sometimes referred to as the American Museum of Arts, but this was all destroyed in the Patent Office fire of 1836. For natural-history objects it wished to have preserved, the United States Government seems to have used chiefly the "cabinet" of the American Philosophical Society and Peale's Museum, both in Philadelphia, and some of President Thomas Jefferson's own natural-history specimens found their way to these places. This was the era, too, of the first of the Government's exploring expeditions to the West—the Lewis and Clark Expedition, Pike's Expedition, General Lewis Cass's Expedition to the Northwest Territories, and Major Stephen H. Long's Expedition to the Rocky Mountains. All these brought back to the East important collections of scientific material, and most of it, also, went to Philadelphia for safekeeping.

There were men, however, who early saw the need for a "national museum" such as other nations of the world could boast of. George Washington had urged his countrymen to "promote . . . institutions for the general diffusion of knowledge." Jefferson was a scientist, museum-minded, and took great pride in the Patent Office. Jefferson's friend Joel Barlow, poet and patriot, had grand ideas about a "national institution" in America for the intellectual advancement of the people, and his elaborate plan, which he circulated throughout the country, embraced the museum idea.

On June 15, 1816, eighty-nine Washington residents formed an association that contained the germ of a national museum. It was first called the Metropolitan Society, but by the time it had received its charter from Congress (on April 20, 1818) its name had been changed to Columbian Institute for the Promotion of Arts and Sciences; and one of its defined objects was "to collect and examine the various mineral productions and natural curiosities of the United States." This society is remembered principally as the first learned society established in Washington, and for its efforts toward the formation of a botanic garden in the Capital. In spite of its many problems, financial and otherwise, it did set up a "cabinet of minerals and a museum of miscellaneous articles." By 1838, however, when its original charter expired, the organization had disintegrated; but in 1840 a somewhat healthier association took its place. This was the National Institution for the Promotion of Science, whose guiding spirit and first president was the Honorable Joel R. Poinsett, of South Carolina.[1] The history of the National Institute, as it was later called, is too long to be detailed here, and has been told by others, but it was a real forerunner of the National Museum, and it was to this organization

[1] G. Brown Goode believed that Poinsett "was, perhaps, better fitted than any of the public men of his time to appreciate the necessity of organizing our public institutions on the most liberal and comprehensive plan . . . Poinsett was the first to suggest the idea of a great national museum at the capital of the nation." Secretary of War under President Martin Van Buren, Poinsett was a man of broad culture and interests. His devotion to science, especially to the science of botany, is commemorated in the name *Poinsettia*, which was first described in 1836 by the Scotch botanist Dr. Robert Graham. In naming this popular plant genus Graham said, "I have dedicated it, if not to its original discoverer, at least to one who has first brought it into cultivation and into general notice among botanists, and from whose exertions many additions to our collections of plants from Mexico are expected." Poinsett died in 1851.

that James Smithson's own cabinet of minerals was entrusted by the Government. Furthermore, at one point when Congress was considering what should be done with Smithson's bequest, it was proposed that the whole legacy be turned over to the newly formed National Institute for management. But the advocates of this proposal, who included Poinsett and other influential men, were outnumbered. Both institutions—the National Institute and the Smithsonian Institution—operated side by side until 1861, when the Institute was dissolved and its collections turned over to the Smithsonian.

In the law incorporating the Smithsonian one provision gave it definite museum functions: "All objects of art and of foreign and curious research, and all objects of natural history, plants, and geological and mineralogical specimens belonging to or hereafter to belong to the United States, which may be in the city of Washington, in whosesoever custody the same may be, shall be delivered to such persons as may be authorized by the Board of Regents to receive them." This would include the so-called "national cabinet of curiosities," which was then housed in the Patent Office Building, but this collection was not removed to the Smithsonian Building until 1857, by which time it had been definitely settled that Congress would make the necessary appropriations for the museum's maintenance. Secretary Henry would rather have seen the museum separate from the Smithsonian. He did not relish the idea of having to depend on annual Government appropriation for Smithsonian activities. It would, he thought, "annually bring the Institution before Congress as a supplicant for government patronage, and ultimately subject it to political influence and control." He wanted the Institution to "mingle its operations as little as possible with those of the general government" and "to ask nothing from Congress except the safe-keeping of its funds." But when he realized that this freedom was not to be, Henry was glad to turn over the Smithsonian's museum to the young and competent hands of Professor Baird, his new Assistant Secretary.

The real nucleus of the museum's natural-history collections was Baird's own hundreds of specimens which he had brought from Carlisle. These included about 2,500 skins (500 species) of North American birds, 1,000 (250 species) of European birds, eggs of about 150 species of North American birds (with many duplicates), and nests and eggs of some 75 species of European birds; skins of the principal mammals of the North and Middle States and of eastern Europe; a collection (more than 500 jars, barrels, etc.) of reptiles, fishes, and amphibians of the United States, and a good collection of the fresh-water fishes and reptiles of central and eastern Europe; embryos of many birds, mammals, and amphibians, skulls and skeletons of numerous North American vertebrates (about 600 specimens), and a large collection of fossil bones from various caves in Pennsylvania and Virginia; and much other material. Years later, in 1888, George Brown Goode wrote: "All the elaborate and efficient methods of administration which are now in use in the National Museum were present, in germ at least, in the little private museum which grew up under his [Baird's] control at home, and which he brought with him in a single freight car, to form the nucleus of the great Smithsonian collections. Among the treasures of this collection, which are still cherished by the Institution, were a number of the choicest bird skins collected by Audubon. . . ."

Another large and important collection that was to come to the Museum (via the National Institute) was that of the United States Exploring Expedition. This Government-sponsored expedition, under Capt. Charles Wilkes, U.S.N., had returned in 1842 from a round-the-world voyage. Sailing in six vessels it had visited the Antarctic regions, South America, Samoa, the Fiji, Hawaiian, and other islands in the Pacific, and the west coast of the United States—with the express purpose of advancing "the great interests of Commerce and Navigation," extending "the boundaries of science," and promoting "the acquisition of knowledge." The expedition included on its staff some of the country's leading scientists; there were naturalists, geologists, botanists, mineralogists, taxidermists, and a philologist. Although actually the primary purpose was to investigate the commercial whaling industry in the Pacific, the expedition yielded important scientific results and brought back a wealth of material for study. Its findings were published in nineteen volumes, of which Wilkes himself wrote the *Narrative* (six volumes), *Hydrography*, and *Meteorology*. The voluminous gatherings of the Wilkes Expedition were placed under the charge of the National Institute in the Patent Office Building and in 1857 were transferred to the Smithsonian.

Baird must have devoted considerable thought to what his department of natural history ought to be and do, for in his first report as Assistant Secretary he outlined what he termed "general suggestions in regard to future operations of the Smithsonian Institution in the Department of Natural History." In line with the general policy of the Institution, he did not intend to duplicate the complete collections of other museums but to concentrate on neglected fields. He wanted the natural history of North America to be best represented; next in importance, he said, was Europe; next to Europe, Japan. He pointed out the museums in the country having major collections, and noted the gaps that ought to be filled. He proposed that collections be procured in any one of six ways—deposits by the Government, deposits by individuals, exchanges, purchases, employment of collectors, and donations. Receipts from all these sources must have been phenomenal, for in 1853 he wrote, "It has been the work of but three years to raise this collection from nothing to the front rank among American cabinets."

It was Baird's purpose, however, not merely to acquire great numbers of miscellaneous specimens but also to accumulate large and representative study collections, "so as to supply all working naturalists with the materials of research." His idea of a natural-history museum was a place where the visitor might gain a knowledge of the fauna and flora of his country, and also a place where the serious student would find ample comparative materials for his researches. He went to great lengths to aid such students and corresponded with scores of them throughout the country. As Dr. Dall has said, "He always seemed to have time for a friendly chat with every newcomer," and "there was hardly a schoolboy of extraordinary genius for bird-nesting or fishing whom he did not know about and encourage." How he found time for all this longhand correspondence is a mystery. Baird at this time was in charge not only of the natural-history collections but also of Smithsonian publications and of the International Exchange Service and did much of the hard and time-consuming work himself. Meanwhile the museum flourished, and specimens of all kinds came in to the Institution from far and wide.

Smithsonian Hospitality

THE ANTEBELLUM WASHINGTON of Baird's early residence there was a vastly different city from that of today. Indeed, it was not a city at all but "a rather shabby Southern village scattered over a grandiose plan." The streets were muddy and unpaved, and grass grew in those less used. There was a slave pen, and domestic animals wandered about. Like today, however, it was noted for its heat in summer, when the "sun heated the rough brick sidewalks to the breaking point." The Bairds lived at that time in a three-story brick house at 918 New York Avenue, N.W. W. H. Dall, Baird's biographer, remarks: "The Smithsonian Building was on the Mall in southwest Washington, known as the 'Island,' because separated by the shallow and odoriferous James Creek canal [also called Tiber Creek] from the main part of town. The Mall had been laid out by A. J. Downing, with fine taste, and was full of shrubbery, grass and trees, but was little cared for, so that in it birds and small beasts found haven. The building was on the south side, facing north; not then quite completed. It was approached by paths and driveways sparsely sprinkled with river gravel and ankle deep in mud on rainy days. The Washington Monument to the west was a mere stump, and the Capitol, to the east, far from being the stately building of the present. It was not a pleasant undertaking then to reach the Smithsonian building on slushy winter days."

The Bairds lived at the New York Avenue address until 1876, when they built a large house at 1445 Massachusetts Avenue, N.W. Their home was a gracious one where visiting men of science were always welcome. The younger naturalists of Washington took advantage of its hospitality and of the privilege of friendship with the man they all esteemed so highly. The Bairds took them under their wing, entertained them in their home on Sunday evenings, and encouraged them in their studies.

Another brand of hospitality was extended to many of these budding scientists [2] by the Smithsonian itself, for they were allowed to occupy the unused upper rooms in the building as lodgings. Especially if the man had no family, he would be allotted one or more of the unused rooms, perhaps in one of the towers, of the then new, brownstone, Gothic-like Smithsonian Building. The geologist Fielding Bradford Meek, for example, lived in a north-tower room from the time he went to Washington in 1858 until his death in 1876. Frank Hamilton Cushing, the noted ethnologist, joined the Smithsonian staff in 1875 and was assigned to rooms in one of the south towers. His friend George Kennan has provided a firsthand account of the sometimes exciting life in the building. He writes (in the *Medina* [N. Y] *Tribune,* December 27, 1923):

In 1878 when I went to Washington to enter the service of the Associated Press, Frank was living near the top of the

2 One group called itself the Megatherium Club.

south tower of the Smithsonian building south of Pennsylvania Avenue. As he had two rooms and two beds, he asked me to come and stay there until I should find a boarding place. . . . I stayed with Frank for several months, partly because it was a pleasure to be with him again, and partly because Dr. Bessels, the scientist of the Hall Arctic expedition, also had a room in the building, and he was another interesting character. Frank and I got our dinners at the restaurant on Pennsylvania Avenue widely known to old Washingtonians as "Harvey's"; but our other meals we took in our rooms. . . .

The room under ours at that time was the workroom of the well known ornithologist Robert Ridgway. It contained hundreds of skins of birds which had been treated with benzene to protect them from insects, and the floor was covered with fragments of wooden boxes, wrapping paper, excelsior, and other combustible material used in packing. The whole room was as inflammable as a powder magazine. One morning Frank happened to want more heat than he could get over a mere cooking lamp, and he thought he would go down and make a fire in Mr. Ridgway's stove. Not noticing on the floor an open can of benzene which the ornithologist had been using, he struck a match. Instantly the vapor in the air flashed out and set fire to the benzene in the can, which sent up a column of flame four or five feet high. In half a minute the can would have been melted apart and the burning benzene would have run all over the tinder-like stuff on the floor. Frank, with perfect self-possession, lifted the blazing can between his hands, carried it steadily across the room without spilling a drop, and set it down in a solid iron coal-scuttle, where it burned itself out without setting fire to anything else.

It may have been that Cushing's presence of mind was inspired by stern fire warnings, for the disastrous fire in the Smithsonian Building had occurred but a dozen or so years before.

Baird as Editor

THE YEAR 1851 saw the completion of Baird's first sizable editorial project, which he had begun while still at Carlisle, acting on the suggestion of his friend George P. Marsh, Smithsonian Regent. For a New York publisher he translated from the German and edited for American readers the then well-known *Bilder Atlas zum Conversations Lexicon.* The work was published in 1852 in four volumes under the title *Iconographic Encyclopaedia of Science, Literature, and Art;* it contained about twelve thousand illustrative engravings, and its consummation entailed a vast amount of editing, rewriting, and collecting in addition to the translating. Its publication brought Baird's name before the public as one of America's foremost scientists, but to Baird perhaps its chief value was the experience he gained in writing and editing and in dealing with authors and publishers, for he was to have much of this type of work to do at the Smithsonian. It also marked him as a prodigious worker, for the whole task was completed in four years. About this time, too, Baird became permanent secretary of the American Association for the Advancement of Science, which had been organized in 1848. This office helped still further to put him in touch with leading scientists in all branches, but it threw additional work on his shoulders, especially in editing and publishing its large annual volumes of *Proceedings.* He was also working on his own researches in American natural history, especially on a catalogue of North American reptiles in the Smithsonian museum. This was his first important publication to bear the Smithsonian imprint. It was published in 1853 in joint authorship with Charles Girard, his assistant.

During the years 1849-50, Capt. Howard Stansbury, U.S.A., had led an exploring and surveying expedition to Great Salt Lake. With the fur trader Jim Bridger as guide, his party of eighteen had explored a new route to the lake, midway between Bear Lake and Echo Canyon trails. They had also taken account of the natural history of the regions traversed, and Stansbury's report, which was published in 1852 as a Senate Document, contained accounts of the zoology, botany, and geology prepared by various naturalists. Baird helped to edit the section on zoology and prepared the parts on the birds, mammals, and (with Girard) reptiles. From time to time he worked with the collections of the Wilkes Exploring Expedition, and he began to take a great interest in the increasing activity in the exploration of the great Western territories.

Exploration Specialist

EVERYONE was talking of the West. The Gold Rush of '49 had taken care of that. The frontier was moving westward at a great pace. The Government, too, was becoming aware of its own size and strength; in order to know what really lay beyond the Mississippi, it took an active role by financing western exploration. Baird made certain that the Smithsonian did all it could to aid and encourage these expeditions. In return it received great numbers of plants, animals, minerals, and ethnological specimens for its museum and had the satisfaction of sharing in the increase of knowledge of our own country. It seemed to be, indeed, a Smithsonian "natural."

It may be useful to list the principal exploring expeditions previous to 1846, when the Institution was founded:

1803, Exploration of Red River by Sibley Expedition
1804, Lewis and Clark Expedition
1805, Zebulon Pike's explorations in Louisiana Territory
1819, Long's Expedition to the Rocky Mountains
1831, Henry R. Schoolcraft's Expedition to the Indian country
1838, United States Exploring Expedition (Wilkes)
1843, Frémont's exploration of Oregon and California

These were only the beginning, and about the time Baird came to Washington exploration was at a high point. The Stansbury Expedition to Great Salt Lake has already been mentioned; in 1852 Capt. Lorenzo Sitgreaves was exploring the region of the Zuñi and Colorado Rivers; the Mexican boundary survey was in progress from

4996

PLATE 16. North front of the National Museum Building (now called the
Arts and Industries Building) as it looked in the eighties

PLATE 17. Samuel Pierpont Langley, third secretary of the Smithsonian Institution, 1887-1906

1854 to 1856 under Maj. W. H. Emory; several parties were in the field engaged in surveying for a railroad route to the Pacific; there were expeditions, also, to other parts of the world—Chile, the La Plata region, the Amazon Valley, Greenland, Bering Sea. In his 1854 Report Baird described twenty-six important explorations undertaken during the preceding two years, including six Pacific Railroad surveys. Of the Smithsonian's part in these he wrote:

With scarcely an exception, every expedition of any magnitude has received more or less aid from the Smithsonian Institution. This has consisted in the supplying of instructions for making observations and collections in meteorology and natural history, and of information as to particular desiderata; in the preparation, in part, of the meteorological, magnetical, and natural history outfit, including the selection and purchase of the necessary apparatus and instruments; in the nomination and training of persons to fill important positions in the scientific corps; in the reception of the collections made, and their reference to individuals competent to report upon them; and in employing skillful and trained artists to make accurate delineations of the new and unfigured species. Much of the apparatus supplied to the different parties was invented or adapted by the Institution for this special purpose, and used for the first time, with results surpassing the most sanguine expectations.

Upon Baird devolved the task of preparing or procuring the reports of many of these expeditions. One of the most important was the report on "Explorations and Surveys for a Railroad Route from the Mississippi River to the Pacific Ocean." Volume 8 on *Mammals,* Volume 9 on *Birds,* and Volume 10 on *Reptiles,* published by Congress in 1857, 1858, and 1859, respectively, were prepared by Baird (the *Birds* in cooperation with two other well-known ornithologists, John Cassin and George N. Lawrence). Scientifically these were important works, not merely routine accounts. Concerning the volume on *Birds,* the naturalist Elliott Coues said, "The appearance of so great a work, from the hands of a most methodical, learned, and sagacious naturalist, aided by two of the leading ornithologists of America, exerted an influence stronger and more widely felt than that of any of its predecessors, Audubon's and Wilson's not excepted, and marked an epoch in the history of American ornithology. . . . Such a monument of original research is like to remain for an indefinite period a source of inspiration to lesser writers, while its authority as a work of reference will always endure." [3]

Collections gathered by the other exploring parties received similar careful scientific study by Baird and his associates. The United States and Mexican Boundary Survey was one of the most notable, and Baird's report on the mammals, reptiles, and birds of this expedition, published in 1859, is classic. It was Baird's task to organize the highly exacting work of study and classification of the specimens brought back to Washington from all corners of the continent. Many of them he described and named himself, and taxonomic literature abounds in new genera and species of animals bearing the name of Baird as describer.

In effect, Baird became, in the course of these years of exploring and biological collecting, adviser to the Government on matters of exploration. One instance of this turned out to be of some national importance. In 1864 the Western Union Telegraph Company undertook a project to run a telegraph line to Europe by way of Alaska and Siberia after the failure of the Atlantic cable. An exploring expedition to British America and Alaska was organized, and through Baird's influence a young man by the name of Robert Kennicott was put in charge of the scientific corps. Kennicott had had previous experience in Alaska, had studied at the Smithsonian under Baird, and was thought to be a promising naturalist. Seven other young men, some of them to attain later distinction as scientists, accompanied Kennicott—Henry M. Bannister, Ferdinand Bischoff, William H. Dall, H. W.

[3] Baird's *Mammals of North America* (1859) and *Birds of North America* (1860), brought out by a private publisher, were special editions of the *Mammals* and *Birds* of the Pacific Railroad Report.

Elliott, G. W. Maynard, Charles Pease, and J. T. Rothrock. They were to make natural-history collections for the Smithsonian Institution and the Chicago Academy of Sciences.

They reached Alaska, as planned, but in May 1866 their leader Kennicott died suddenly of a heart attack near Nulato. Furthermore, soon afterward the trans-Atlantic cable was assured of success and completed, and as a result the Western Union dropped the whole matter of an overland telegraph line, and the survey party was disbanded. However, they had, in their few months in the Far North, done a remarkable work. They had penetrated territory never before seen or traversed by white men. One party explored the Yukon along the unknown stretch of river between Nulato and Fort Yukon. Others explored equally important areas of *terra incognita* westward to Bering Sea.

One of the Kennicott party—H. M. Bannister—returned to Washington in 1867 just about the time that the purchase of Alaska from Russia was being hotly debated in Congress, and he proved to be probably the only man in the Capital possessing firsthand knowledge of Alaska. He and Baird were called into consultation by Secretary of State Seward and Senator Sumner, and also testified before the Senate committee that was holding hearings on the proposed Alaska purchase. They were able to furnish information that must have been convincing. As one writer has summarized it: "Baird pointed out the wealth of furs, fish, and timber, and showed that gold and copper had been found in the Territory, and that agricultural crops could be raised there. Apparently practically all the specific information regarding the value of the Territory, including the usefulness of Sitka Harbor as a base for naval vessels, was supplied either by the Smithsonian Institution or by men who had worked in Alaska under its auspices." Bannister himself later remarked: "The annexation was ridiculed at the time but we could testify that the country was worth the price asked. Time has sufficiently proved that we were right and I can safely say that we did not overstate anything. . . . The project of the Western Union Telegraph Company of an overland telegraph across Bering Straits to Europe was a failure but its greatest result was the annexation of Alaska."

The United States Fish Commission

ALTHOUGH there was scarcely any branch of natural history on which Baird was not an authority (this was before the days of minute specialization among scientists), mammals, birds, and reptiles had been his chief fields of study up to this time. About 1870, however, he began to devote more attention to the study of fishes; this was not a new interest by any means, for he had already published a number of ichthyological papers, mostly in collaboration with his assistant, Charles Girard. Summer visits to the Atlantic coast, both in New Jersey and Massachusetts, had brought to his attention the alarming decrease of food fishes taking place, and he now was convinced that a thorough investigation of these fisheries was needed. He persuaded Secretary Henry to allot $100 from Smithsonian funds for the study, and the Treasury Department furnished a thirty-foot yacht, the *Mazeppa*. This was the beginning of the United States Fish Commission, which Baird fathered from its very start, even to the extent of furnishing quarters for its work in his own house.

The resolution establishing the Commission, which Baird helped to draft, was passed by Congress early in 1871. It provided that the President appoint "from among the civil officers or employees of the Government, one person of proved scientific and practical acquaintance with the fishes of the coast, to be Commissioner of Fish and Fisheries, to serve without additional salary." There was only one logical person for the job, and Baird was appointed Fish Commissioner by President Grant on February 25, 1871. His duties as Commissioner, which he undertook in addition to his work at the Smithsonian, were prescribed as follows: "To prosecute investigations and inquiries . . . with a view of ascertaining whether any and what diminution in the number of food fishes of the coast and the lakes of the United States has taken place; and if so, to what causes the same is due; and, also, whether any and what protective, prohibitory, or precautionary measures should be adopted in the premises, and to report upon the same to Congress."

Here again one must pause to pay tribute to Baird as a prodigious worker and to his ability to enlist the help of others in important but meagerly financed scientific studies. By June 1871 he had established headquarters for the new Commission at Woods Hole, Mass., situated on the elbow of Cape Cod, and had gathered a group of voluntary assistants to help in the biological work to be undertaken. He encouraged visiting naturalists to participate and invited students of zoology to come to Woods Hole to make collections of marine life and pursue their researches which were germane to the Commission's interests. In fact, the laboratory at Woods Hole soon became a favorite and noted mecca for zoologists, who would come at their own expense to take advantage of the unusual opportunities offered for scientific work. Reciprocally, the Commission and hence the Government benefited. The Woods Hole Laboratory lived on, however, long after the Fish Commission ended its work there—a veritable "marine university" and a memorial to the arduous labors of Baird. In 1902 (on a granite boulder near the water at Woods Hole) the American Fisheries Society placed a bronze tablet "in memory of Spencer Fullerton Baird, U. S. Commissioner of Fisheries, 1871-1887 . . . in appreciation of his estimable services to Ichthyology, Fish Culture and the Fisheries."

Volumes could be written on the work of the Fish Commission, whose job it has been to conduct its scientific work toward the definite and practical results of maintaining an important food supply for the nation. Secretary Langley, the year after Baird's death, praised the early work of the Commission. He wrote to a prominent

Senator: "It seems hardly necessary to dwell upon the results in fish-culture attained by the commission under Professor Baird's direction. You are thoroughly familiar with the manner in which certain fisheries, such as the shad fishery on the Atlantic coast, the salmon fishery of the Pacific coast, and the whitefish fishery of the Great Lakes, have been saved from destruction; how the Asiatic carp has been planted in the 20,000 or more ponds and lakes in almost every township in the United States; how the shad fishery has been established in unfamiliar waters, such as the Ohio River and the Pacific Ocean; and in addition to this, how many other steps of great magnitude have been made in the art of fish-culture. I dare not attempt to estimate the practical value of the work of the Commission to the country, but can not doubt that it amounts to very many millions of dollars. . . . No one can question that the peculiar excellence of [this] work of our Government has been directly or indirectly due to the presence of Professor Baird at the head of the Commission. He had no rivals, and during his administration no word of criticism was ever uttered by competent persons."

Whole books, too, could be, and have been, written on the voyages of the *Albatross, Fish Hawk,* and other vessels sent out at various times by the Fish Commission for deep-sea exploration. The scientific results of these expeditions are inestimable, and the collections dredged and brought back by them, not only of fishes from many parts of the globe, but also of other forms of marine life, have been an almost inexhaustible source of zoological study. In 1903 the Fish Commission, renamed the Bureau of Fisheries, was made a full bureau of the Government and placed under the administration of the Department of Commerce and Labor. In 1941, in the interests of Government reorganization, its functions were combined with those of the Bureau of Biological Survey to form the Fish and Wildlife Service of the Department of the Interior. Thus the work of the "Fish Commission" still goes on, after three-quarters of a century, a monument to the pioneering and hard work of Spencer F. Baird. It was another instance of the Smithsonian Institution's "starting something"—something that, like the Weather Bureau, grew beyond the borders of its infant home, to be adopted by the Government to serve the people as long as they needed it.

The Bureau of American Ethnology

JUST AS the Fish Commission developed from the foresight and persistence of one man, Spencer Baird, so did another Federal agency, the Bureau of American Ethnology, arise. But this bureau, unlike the Weather Bureau and the Fish Commission, was attached permanently to the Institution, and is today completing its three-score years and ten as a part of the Smithsonian family. Because it came into being during Baird's secretaryship and had its genesis in the Government's exploration work so near to his heart, a little of its history may appropriately be included here.

John Wesley Powell, the man who founded the Bureau of Ethnology, may perhaps be best described as a "war horse." He was a little of everything—explorer, geologist, anthropologist, philosopher, poet. In science he was the synthesizer and organizer rather than the analyst. He was a man who made enemies as well as friends, but in the nearly half-century since his death his stature has increased rather than diminished.

A couple of years after the Civil War (in which he lost his right arm at Shiloh) Powell, then a young naturalist and professor of geology at Illinois Wesleyan University at Bloomington, organized a party of sixteen "naturalists, students, and amateurs" to explore the mountain region of Colorado. This proved to be but a preliminary trip. The next summer (1868) he returned to Colorado with another party (including his wife) and continued exploration, this time with the support of the Smithsonian and various Illinois institutions, and spent the following winter at a camp in the White River Valley. From it Powell made excursions to the Green, Grand, and Yampa Rivers, and began his studies of Indian tribes. He became greatly interested in the geology and geography of the Colorado River. The general course of this immense river system was then known, but there were great tracts of the Colorado River country that white men had never set eyes on, that even the early Spanish explorers had missed. No one—least of all a scientist—had ever gone through the Grand Canyon and lived to tell of it. This very thing Powell resolved to do, and he returned East to get financial support for his next expedition.

Congress made an appropriation for the project, and it was placed under the direction of the Smithsonian. Authority was also given Powell to obtain rations for his men from various western military posts. With ten men in four boats, the party embarked on May 24, 1869, "where the Union Pacific Railroad crosses the Green River in southwestern Wyoming; followed the Green River through deep gorges in the Uinta Mountains to its junction in open country with the Grand River, below which point the name Colorado is given; then continued down the Colorado through its profound canyons in the plateaus of southwestern Utah and northern Arizona to the open country near the Nevada line on August 29"—this from W. M. Davis, one of Powell's biographers. But this historic boat trip was more dramatic than Mr. Davis's succinct account would indicate. The expedition was a great success, and Powell was hailed as an intrepid pioneer— the first white man (one-armed at that) to conquer the "invincible" Grand Canyon of the Colorado and make its incredible wonders known to the world. "The exploration," wrote one commentator, "was the boldest in design and the most perilous in execution among the scientific expeditions recorded in the annals of the nation." Powell's western explorations were, indeed, so impressive that Congress continued financial aid for them, under the

Smithsonian. The Government benefited by the new geological, geographical, and ethnological knowledge of the West that resulted. Powell was one of the first to see the possibilities of irrigation in making the desert regions of the West productive, and his report to Congress in 1878 on "Lands of the Arid Region of the United States" was pioneering.

Paralleling Major Powell's explorations in the Rocky Mountain region, which extended from 1869 to 1872, other Government surveys were in progress. These were the United States Geological and Geographical Surveys of the Territories, under Prof. F. V. Hayden; the United States Geographic Surveys West of the One-Hundredth Meridian, under Lt. George M. Wheeler; and the Survey of the Fortieth Parallel, under Clarence King. To all these the Smithsonian lent whatever aid it could. These various surveys, however, productive as they were, began to rival and compete with one another, and Congress, at the suggestion of Powell, deemed it wise to reorganize the whole Federal exploration work. It abolished the Wheeler, Hayden, and Powell surveys and in 1879 made appropriations for two Government bureaus to carry on their functions —the United States Geological Survey under the Interior Department and the Bureau of Ethnology under the Smithsonian Institution. Clarence King was made director of the Geological Survey, and Major Powell director of the Bureau of Ethnology. In 1881 King resigned, and Powell conducted both bureaus until 1894, when he resigned his directorship of the Geological Survey. He continued as chief of the Bureau of American Ethnology until his death on September 23, 1902.

It was natural that this new agency of the Government, concerned with the science of man, or anthropology, should be attached to the Smithsonian, for from its very beginning the Institution had fostered this subject. Professor Henry had encouraged it, and, as we have seen, the Institution's very first publication, in 1848, *Ancient Monuments of the Mississippi Valley,* by Squier and Davis, had been a monograph in archeology. Two years later the Institution published a similar work by Squier, on *Aboriginal Monuments of the State of New York*. In 1852 appeared a 400-page quarto volume, a *Grammar and Dictionary of the Dakota Language,* which was followed in 1858 by a similar compendium of the Yoruba language. These were the first of many in the field of philology, or linguistics, a branch of anthropology. When, in 1882, the Institution published a complete catalogue of its publications issued during its first thirty-five years, fifty-nine publications were listed under the headings Anthropology and Philology. One of the most important of these was *Systems of Consanguinity and Affinity of the Human Family,* by Lewis Henry Morgan (616 pp., 1869), a basic study of primitive society.

The Government-sponsored surveys and explorations of the western territories provided a stimulus to American ethnology. Everywhere the explorers went they found either the remains of human habitations and cultures or the living Indians themselves. We had not become too solicitous for the interests of the red man. We were still having trouble with him (three members of Powell's exploring party down the Colorado River had been killed by Paiutes),[4] but still if the "savages" were to become the wards of the United States Government, ought not the Government to know something about their stepchildren? Some of the tribes, too, were disappearing, and scholars were beginning to be concerned over the problem of recording their languages, myths, religions, arts, songs, and other parts of their culture before they had forever disappeared. Powell's new bureau had virtually a virgin field before it. Even the science of anthropology itself was young, and some doubted even whether it was a science at all. But Powell's ability as an organizer was soon felt,

4 Powell's magnanimous attitude toward the Indian is illustrated in his statement, "When I stand before the sacred fire of an Indian village and listen to the red man's philosophy, no anger stirs my blood. I love him as one of my kind."

and the bureau, both through its own staff and through its collaborators, began to turn out important works of research in three branches of anthropology—archeology, linguistics, and ethnology. And throughout the years, combining field work with historical and bibliographic research, it has continued to produce them, in a way that would be gratifying to the American taxpayer if he were aware of it.

After seventy years the Bureau's staff is little larger than it was in the early days, but it has gone on unostentatiously, carrying out its one aim as a branch of the Smithsonian—to increase and diffuse anthropological knowledge of the aboriginal American people. On its scientific staff it has claimed such names as W J ("no period") McGee; William Henry Holmes (chief of the Bureau from 1902 to 1910); Frederick Webb Hodge (1910 to 1918); J. Walter Fewkes (1918 to 1928); Henry Wetherbee Henshaw; Cyrus Thomas; James Mooney; Paul Radin; J. N. B. Hewitt; Truman Michelson; and John R. Swanton. One of the high marks of the Bureau's achievement was the publication, in 1907 and 1910, of the two-volume *Handbook of the American Indians North of Mexico,* under the editorship of F. W. Hodge, a monumental work that has taken its place as a standard reference for students in many fields. Worthy of mention also are the *Handbook of American Indian Languages* (also in two volumes), *Handbook of the Indians of California,* and the recent *Handbook of South American Indians* (six volumes).

The Bureau of American Ethnology and the National Museum have worked together. The National Museum developed its own department of anthropology, but its primary concern was to arrange displays of anthropological material for the visiting public, such as life-size Indian groups, and to build up large reserve collections and make them available for study by those engaged in original researches. The Bureau, on the other hand, has not been encumbered with museum functions, and is required by law to turn over to the National Museum all its archeological and ethnological materials when it has finished studying them. Its field work among the various tribes and at archeological sites has yielded thousands of specimens in the nature of artifacts, skeletal remains, and cultural objects. The work of the two units has thus dovetailed rather than conflicted, and the result has been to make the Smithsonian Institution a world leader in the study of man on the earth.

Baird himself was not an anthropologist, yet so broad was his knowledge of all things pertaining to the natural world that the science of man could not have been excluded. The Government explorations and surveys, in which he had so important a part, as the man behind the scenes, so to speak, were rich sources of new anthropologic knowledge, and it was during his secretaryship that this phase of the Institution's activities received perhaps its greatest impetus.

Expositions and the Smithsonian

FOLLOWING THE RECONSTRUCTION PERIOD after the Civil War, as the country attempted to resume its economic stability, it began to take stock of itself. There seemed to be a national urge to celebrate America's progress in industry, agriculture, the arts, science, and invention, and during the decade from 1876 to 1886 a series of expositions, some of them international in scope, were held in various cities throughout the United States. The first and largest of these was the Philadelphia Centennial, or World's Fair, of 1876, celebrating the one-hundredth anniversary of the Declaration of Independence. This was followed by the Philadelphia International Exhibition of Sheep and Wool Products, 1880; the National Mining and Industrial Exposition at Denver in 1882; the Atlanta Exposition of 1882; the New York Exposition of 1883, celebrating the one-hundredth anniversary of the treaty of peace after the Revolutionary War; the Southern Exposition at Louisville in 1884; the Cincinnati Industrial

Exposition of 1884; the World's Industrial and Cotton Centennial Exposition in New Orleans in 1884; and the Minneapolis Industrial Exposition in 1886. In all of these meetings various branches of the Government were called upon to participate, and for the Smithsonian these were busy exposition years. In addition, various expositions were being held abroad, and in these, too, the Institution took part.

The Centennial Exposition at Philadelphia, however, was the greatest event of its kind ever held up to that time; and, as it turned out, it proved to be an important landmark in Smithsonian history. Congress appropriated sizable sums to enable the various Government agencies, including the Smithsonian and the Fish Commission, to enter extensive exhibits demonstrating their functions, and Professor Baird was a member of the board appointed by President Grant to have general direction of the Government's participation. The Exposition opened on May 19, 1876, with every important foreign country represented, and for six months people trekked to Philadelphia to see the great show. And it was, indeed, a great liberal education, giving little-traveled Americans a chance to see how the rest of the world lived and also how their own now century-old nation compared with other nations in industrial, scientific, and social progress. Even as the Exposition was being held, the Indians under Sitting Bull were making their last stand against the White Man, and though they killed General Custer's cavalry to the last man, the battle marked the end of the Indian resistance. The first hundred years had been hard. Now "progress" was the word, and the Exposition helped Americans grasp its meaning. The machine age was here in earnest, and thousands of the Fair visitors must indeed have felt its impact when they witnessed President Grant and Emperor Dom Pedro of Brazil start the 4,000-horsepower Corliss steam engine in Machinery Hall, which ran all the machinery of the Exposition.

The Centennial closed on November 10. Both Secretary

Henry and Professor Baird had anticipated the next question: What was to be done with the many Federal and State exhibits, as well as those of some of the foreign countries? Presentation to the National Museum was the logical answer, and they began making plans for the reception of these exhibits. Of the foreign exhibits, Henry reported that "the best and most important were presented to the United States at the close of the exhibition, embracing many complete series of objects, illustrating the geology, metallurgy, and ethnology, and the general resources of the nations. Of about forty governments and colonies, the choicest of the exhibits of thirty-four were presented to the Smithsonian Institution for the National Museum." In addition, "several entire State exhibits and many belonging to private parties" were donated. "Nevada, Montana, and Utah presented the whole of the mineral exhibits, while partial exhibits were received from several other States and Territories." Even though some of these donations were the result of Baird's solicitation, they were none the less valuable on that account. Baird worked always with the future of the National Museum foremost in his mind.

It was unthinkable, however, that the Smithsonian Building could accommodate this museum "bonanza," and before the end of 1876 Congress was asked for an appropriation of $250,000 for a new museum building. Action was not taken, however, until 1879. In the meantime, Secretary Henry died, and the task of seeing the new building through was one of the first devolving upon Baird as the new Secretary. The erection of the building (with Gen. William T. Sherman as chairman of the building commission) was started on April 17, 1879, and completed in 1881 in time (though still unoccupied) for the inaugural reception and ball for President Garfield on March 4. The "temporary" structure, covering two and a third acres directly east of the Smithsonian Institution Building, was cheaply built and did not turn out to be a paragon of architectural beauty. Though it was adequate only for a brief time for the rapidly growing museum collections, it has never been replaced. Today, crowded "to the gunwales" with an array of the Nation's treasures in all departments of the arts and industries and in American history—from George Washington's field kit to Wiley Post's *Winnie Mae*—it presents something less than an idea of a modern, well-organized, well-lighted museum of science and industry. But something should perhaps be said for a building (even an ugly one) that served its original emergency purpose so well and at so small a public expense. It was the cheapest building ever erected by the Government in Washington, per cubic foot of space. Its erection was a milestone in the development of the National Museum.

Baird's Contributions

SPENCER F. BAIRD'S CONNECTION with the Smithsonian extended over a period of thirty-seven years—twenty-eight as Assistant Secretary and nine as Secretary—and during that time it is doubtful whether he ever made a single personal enemy. As a scientist he had the highest respect of his colleagues. "No man," wrote Dall as late as 1927, "has more greatly contributed to the promotion of science in America than Professor Baird." And as a personality he was equally great. There are a few veteran naturalists alive today who remember him as a modest, genial, and lovable character. In February, 1947, then nearing his ninety-first birthday, my friend Dr. Albert Kenrick Fisher,[5] the ornithologist, wrote me: "Among the people with whom I have associated during a fairly active life, few have impressed me more favorably than Professor Baird. I think he had a better understanding of the proper treatment of mankind than most people. He was sincere, kind, and unselfish. His wonderful personality engendered interest and enthusiasm among Government scientific workers,

5 Dr. Fisher died on June 12, 1948, after this was written.

including those in far-off army posts, so that scientific work rapidly increased during his period of influence. I have always regretted that I did not meet him earlier."

Baird was shy in nature, never putting himself forward, but when occasion arose he was a convincing speaker. "His ability as a talker and organizer," wrote G. Brown Goode, "was never better seen than when [he was] . . . in the presence of Congressional committees, before whom he was summoned from year to year to give reasons for his requests for money to be used in expanding the work of the Fish Commission or the National Museum. He was always received by the members with the heartiest welcome; and it seemed that always these pushing, brusque men of business, who ordinarily rushed with the greatest of haste through the routine of committee work, forgot their usual hurry when Professor Baird was before them. They listened attentively as long as he could be induced to talk about his plans for the development of the organization whose success he had at heart. Not infrequently they would wander from the business before them as they asked him questions upon subjects which his suggestive remarks impressed upon their attention."

In Washington Baird's associations were widespread and diverse. In 1878 he was one of a group of sixty congenial Washingtonians who founded the Cosmos Club, and the next year he served as its first regular president. The club was organized "as a social experiment," to be composed of men devoted to or interested in science, literature, or art, professionally or otherwise, and this was broad enough to include all manner of scientists, as well as writers, physicians, surgeons, lawyers, educators, librarians, engineers, and army and naval men. Among the cofounders with Baird were men as diversified in their interests as Henry Adams, author; Daniel Coit Gilman, President of Johns Hopkins University; John W. Powell, ethnologist; and John Jay Knox, Comptroller of the Currency. The selection of Baird as first president attested to the high regard in which he was held by those with whom

PLATE 18. The Smithsonian Building from the south, showing paddocks where animals were kept prior to the establishment of the National Zoological Park in 1890. Because of intervening structures, this view would today be impossible

PLATE 19.   View of the Smithsonian Building and the Smithsonian Park from the north, at the turn of the century

PLATE 20.   Fuselage of Langley Aerodrome "A" mounted on launching car atop houseboat. Charles M. Manly is standing in the pilot's nacelle; the engine is directly behind him. Potomac River, Fall of 1903

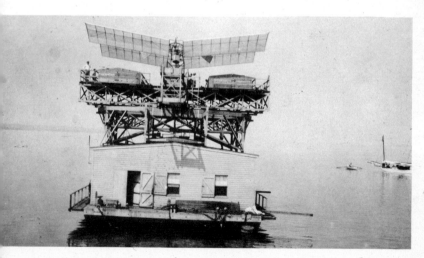

PLATE 21.   Langley Aerodrome "A" assembled and mounted on launching track atop houseboat. Front view. Potomac River, Fall of 1903

PLATE 22. Langley one-quarter size gasoline-engined model aerodrome. This was the seventh in the series of large models developed by Langley to test his ideas. This model, believed to have been the first heavier-than-air device to accomplish flight with a gasoline engine, was made to exactly one-fourth scale of the larger terodrome "A," and with it the details of construction, rigging, balance, and aerodynamic characteristics were worked out. The model was successfully tested on August 8, 1903, when it flew a distance of about 1,000 feet, remaining in the air 27 seconds

he chose to associate. Also, this selection, as Dall describes it, "dissipated the suspicions of some perturbed individuals who had seen in the formation of the club a scheme to influence Congress and create a scientific cabal intended to control governmental scientific activities." Such subversiveness was alien to Baird's makeup, and official Washington knew it.

When Baird died, on August 19, 1887, following a long period of overwork and heart strain, America lost what many thought was its greatest naturalist. Certainly the National Museum lost the best friend it ever had, and Washington lost one of the most self-effacing public officials of all time. When the German Fishery Union learned of his death, it issued a circular in appreciation of his work, closing with this simple but sincere tribute: "Im Herzen seiner deutschen wie seiner amerikanischen Freunde wird er lange, lange fortleben. *Ave, cara anima!*" ("In the hearts of his German as well as his American friends he will long, long live. Farewell, beloved Soul!") There were many eulogies to follow, but perhaps none more indicative of the esteem in which he was held the world over.

In November following Baird's death the secretaryship of the Smithsonian Institution passed to Samuel Pierpont Langley, an astronomer, whose name, also, was to become known throughout the world even as Henry's and Baird's were. But he will be the subject of a later chapter.

6

GEORGE BROWN GOODE,
THE YOUNG GENIUS

POSSIBLY no man connected with the Smithsonian Institution has possessed such a marked ability to pick sound and capable assistants as Spencer Fullerton Baird. He was quick to perceive the latent worth of a man. Just as at Cambridge Louis Agassiz, by virtue of his magnetic personality and unique teaching methods, attracted a whole school of American students of natural history, so Baird at Washington gathered around him a coterie of young and promising talent. Baird, of course, was their master, and together they became known as "the Bairdian school," characterized by exactitude in scientific statement, conciseness in deduction, and careful analysis of data, in contrast to many of the older European naturalists whose statements often had to be taken without benefit of documentary substantiation.

One man who came to the Smithsonian under Baird's aegis was, indeed, a genius, especially remarkable for his broad and humane interests and for the quality and quantity of scientific and literary work that he performed in his brief forty-five years of life. If George Brown Goode had lived, quite likely he would have become Secretary of the Smithsonian. David Starr Jordan said: "Of all American naturalists, Doctor Goode was the most methodical, the most conscientious, and in his way, the most artistic. And of them all no one was more beloved by his fellows." It was, as Secretary S. P. Langley remarked, "incomprehensible that one man could accomplish so much in one single life."

Background and Training

GOODE was born at New Albany, Indiana, on February 13, 1851, of sturdy American stock. His mother, Sarah Woodruff Crane, died in the boy's infancy. He passed his early youth at Amenia, in eastern New York, where his father had moved after retiring from his mercantile business. We are told that Francis Collier Goode, the father, was of studious habits and keen observation and that he bore a strong facial resemblance to Henry Clay. Though he lacked a professional education, he was generally well informed. A friend said of him: "Few public men are better acquainted with the political history of the United States, and few naturalists more enthusiastic lovers of nature, or more familiar with the habit and appearance of plants." These characteristics he passed on to his son. It is of interest, too, that in his library he had a set of Smithsonian *Reports,* and from these young George first became attracted to science and learned of the Institution he was later to serve.

In 1870, when he was only a little past nineteen, Goode was graduated from Wesleyan University at Middletown, Connecticut, with a decided penchant and talent for natural history. The same year he began postgraduate work at Harvard College under Louis Agassiz and so distinguished himself with the Professor that he was recommended for the position of curator of the university museum in the Judd Hall of Natural Science at Middletown. This building had just been presented to Wesleyan University by Orange Judd, the pioneer agricultural journalist and Goode's future father-in-law. Goode undertook the arrangement of the natural-science collections and gained an experience in museum administration and techniques that was to prove a solid foundation in later years. He was then only about twenty years old, a stout and healthy lad, prodigiously doing the work of an older man and doing it well.

His first appearances in print consisted of various short notes in the *College Argus* and *College Review,* but his maiden scientific paper, "The Billfish in Fresh Water" (i.e., the Connecticut River), appeared as a brief note in the *American Naturalist* in September 1871. At the Portland meeting of the American Association for the Advancement of Science in 1873 he presented a paper on the question "Do Snakes Swallow Their Young?" and this, Goode's first important contribution to zoology, was published the next year in the *Proceedings* of the Association.

In 1872, through the influence of his stepmother, he met Professor Baird at Eastport, Maine—a meeting that proved to be a turning point in his life. The following year, at the Portland meeting of the A.A.A.S., the two met again, and Baird, at once recognizing Goode's genuine potentialities, invited him to participate in the work of the United States Fish Commission, which was then beginning to take shape under Baird's organizing genius. Thus the young man began a volunteer service for the Commission that lasted several years, during which he collected fishes along the eastern coast, wrote papers on what he was learning about them, and became not only a specialist in technical ichthyology but also a student of the economic problems relating to fisheries and the fishing industry. Upon Baird's invitation he spent the winter of 1873 in Washington arranging the fish specimens at the

Smithsonian. Here he met Secretary Joseph Henry and partook of the Henrys' hospitality and encouragement.

Although Goode kept his official connection with Wesleyan University until 1877, the Fish Commission and the Smithsonian gradually claimed him. He was given the title of curator of the museum. In 1876 appeared his first publication under the Smithsonian imprint—*Catalogue of the Fishes of the Bermudas,* a bulletin (No. 5) of the National Museum, based on a trip he had made to these islands four years earlier. This was the beginning of two decades of unremitting hard work for the Institution to which he became singularly devoted.

On November 27, 1877, he was married to Sarah Ford Judd, only daughter of Orange Judd, and a woman who shared his love of nature. As Secretary Langley has recorded, Goode was "eminently a domestic man, finding the highest joys that life brought him with his family and children." This devotion to family extended to a keen interest in genealogy, especially that of the Goode family, and impelled him to work twenty-five years preparing his book *Virginia Cousins,* which, as the title page painstakingly explained, was "A Study of the Ancestry and Posterity of John Goode of Whitby, a Virginia Colonist of the Seventeenth Century, with notes upon Related Families, a Key to Southern Genealogy and a History of the English Surname Gode, Goad, Goode, or Good from 1148 to 1887." This work, begun as a hobby, turned out to be a fine and model piece of genealogical scholarship. He saw the sociological and historical significance of genealogies, and accordingly was determined that his history of the Goode family should be as nearly perfect as it was in his power to make it. "Every man," he quoted Emerson as saying, "is a bundle of ancestors," and then inserted a special excursus "for the future use of the four little bundles at this moment sheltered beneath his roof-tree," referring to his four children, a daughter and three sons, the eldest then about nine years of age. In Washington the family had a home on Lanier Heights, on a street overlooking the area of the Rock Creek Valley that was then being developed into the National Zoological Park.

Early Years with the Smithsonian

ONE of the first big jobs that Goode undertook after becoming established at the Institution was to help Secretary Baird organize and execute the Smithsonian and Fish Commission exhibit at the Philadelphia Centennial Exposition in 1876. They saw in this Exposition a great opportunity to bring the scientific work of the Federal Government to the attention of thousands of people. They wanted to show especially what a great national museum could mean to a nation, culturally as well as scientifically. For this was, in fact, a crucial time for the National Museum. Although the Smithsonian from its very beginning had been delegated to provide for a national museum, Congress had not been generous in appropriating funds for its upkeep. This treatment was particularly unfortunate in view of the great influx of material from the United States Exploring Expedition under Capt. Charles Wilkes and from the explorations of our Western Territories. Only about $4,000 a year was being appropriated to care for the collections; there was, therefore, little chance of expansion; and in 1858 Secretary Henry said: "It will, therefore, be the policy of the Institution, unless other means are provided, to confine the collections to illustrations of the products of the North American continent."

The future of the National Museum was close to the hearts of Baird and Goode, and they were quick to take advantage of the publicity afforded by the Centennial Exposition. As Langley has recorded, Baird was "determined that the exhibition made by the United States should bear witness to what the Museum could do. . . . The Government made a loan of several millions to the Exposition, which no one then supposed would ever be repaid. Members of the appropriations committee felt quite safe in jokingly assuring Professor Baird that if the money was repaid an appropriation for a National Museum building should not be withheld. The entire staff of the Museum, including several unpaid volunteers, with Goode at their head, gave all their energies for nearly a year to make the Government and especially the Museum exhibits a success, feeling that the future of the Museum was at stake. Individuals all over the country were called upon to assist by advice or material in their special lines. Thousands of letters were written and thousands of exhibits gathered. Here Goode had his first training in the arts of exhibition, in which he finally became the acknowledged master. Many were the discussions as to system, selection of exhibits, cases, labels, and method in general. It was indeed a liberal education to those engaged in the work. . . . The result was a glorious success, acknowledged by all beholders."

The part of the exhibit that Goode directed was unified under the general theme "Animal Resources of the United States." He prepared an elaborate classification and catalogue of all the objects that made up the display. In addition, there was an exhibition of minerals and another of ethnologic materials.

Director of the Museum

IMPORTANT, too, was the fact that Goode was kept thinking seriously and deeply on the problem of museum organization and administration, so that when the new museum building was completed in 1881 he was ready with a well-considered plan for a public museum. By that time he had been made Assistant Secretary of the Smithsonian, in direct charge of the United States National Museum, and was recognized as a leading museum authority. And Secretary Baird gave him free rein in developing his ideas. A national museum, Goode believed, should serve a threefold function. First, it should be *a museum of record,* in which is preserved "the material foundation of an enormous amount of scientific knowledge." Second, it should be *a museum of research,* "which aims to make its contents serve in the highest degree as a stimulus to inquiry and a foundation for scientific investigation." Third, it should be *an educational museum,* "through its policy of illustrating, by specimens, every kind of natural object and every manifestation of human thought and activity." This was the ideal he set up for the National Museum, which he directed.

But he went beyond that. He developed a philosophy of museum administration that was broad and sound and made the conduct of a museum virtually a science in itself. And in this he demonstrated the originality, thoroughness, foresight, and organizing ability that made him a genius in his line. Many of the principles he laid down and the organization plans he codified are still effective today. The secret perhaps was, as it has been in many another man's success, that he believed wholeheartedly in what he was doing—he was certain of the efficacy of the museum as a cultural agency. He summed up his principles in these positive words: "The degree of civilization to which any nation, city, or province has attained is best shown by the character of its public museums and the liberality with which they are maintained."

Possibly we need to be reminded that museum exhibition techniques and methods have changed considerably since Goode's day. As Clifford C. Gregg, director of the Chicago Natural History Museum, recently wrote in the *Museum News:* "Our emphasis was then on cataloging and arranging materials, classifying them and describing them. We achieved orderly and, in many cases, attractive displays. Our interpretation was through descriptive labels in our exhibition collections, and through publication of our scientific studies. This procedure was, I believe, in keeping with the times, and in certain instances perhaps ahead of its time. However, times change. The cultural level of the general public and its knowledge within the fields of our operations have increased considerably." The aims and principles of museums, as formulated by Goode, are still the same. The program is still "research, record, and the dissemination of knowledge."

Goode differed from many museum administrators in being able to bring to bear upon his work a phenomenal breadth of learning and variety of interests. He was a true scholar, one who was able not only to apply himself with distinction to a specialized field (in this instance ichthyology), but also to see the necessity for the integration of all knowledge of whatever kind and from whatever source; and certainly in him the aspirations of James Smithson found a staunch protagonist. To quote Langley again: "He had a strong interest in literature, and wrote in an excellent English style—clear, direct, and unpretentious. I have never met a mind in touch with more far-away and disconnected points than his, nor one of the same breadth and variety of writing, outside the range of his own specialty. He had fine aesthetic tastes and derived keen enjoyment from everything that was beautiful in nature or in art. He knew all natural sights and sounds, and recognized the note of every bird. . . ."

I have talked with men who knew George Brown Goode, and with one accord they have characterized him in the highest terms. They remembered him, after fifty years, as a man of great and generous spirit, of sterling and loyal character. He apparently possessed that none-too-common ability to make people like him and at the same time to maintain firm control over those under him. "He had a hearty way of meeting associates . . . ," wrote Theodore N. Gill, a colleague at the Institution, "but in spite of his gentleness, firmness and vigor in action became manifest when occasion called for them."

Goode's contributions to science were manifold. His first loyalty in line of research was to the study of fishes, and in spite of his increasing administrative duties he turned out dozens of substantial ichthyological papers, many of them published in the *Proceedings* and *Bulletins* of the National Museum and many of them written in coauthorship with Tarleton Hoffman Bean, who was then the Museum's curator of fishes.[1] The culmination of this collaboration was the publication of *Oceanic Ichthyology,* a treatise on the deep-sea and pelagic fishes of the world, based chiefly on the collections made by the steamers *Blake, Albatross,* and *Fish Hawk* in the northwestern Atlantic. This work comprised two large quarto volumes, which appeared in the year of Goode's death, 1896, as a *Special Bulletin* of the National Museum. It was, as David Starr Jordan said, "Goode's most important scientific study" and showed "a distinct advance over all other treatises of abyssal fishes. . . ." In it 156 new species and 55 new genera of fishes belonging to the Atlantic abyssal fauna were first named.

Only once did Goode try his hand at purely popular writing on fishes. This was his book *American Fishes: A Popular Treatise upon the Game and Food Fishes of North America, with Special Reference to Habits and Methods of Capture,* published in 1888 and widely reviewed at home and abroad. Here he showed himself to be a literary artist as well as a scientist, and succeeded in his expressed ambition to write a book that "people would buy and read" rather than a technical reference work, however fundamental, for specialized and esoteric readers. And many a Government scientist will understand his feeling when he wrote that up to that time it had been his lot to have all the products of his pen published in those "dismal looking bunches of papers known as public documents, which of necessity must be classified among Charles Lamb's 'books which are not books.' "

But Goode ultimately, perhaps, will be remembered as a historian and organizer of science rather than as a scientist. It was well enough, he thought, to catalogue biological specimens, to work over collections and prepare taxonomic treatises, to map the distribution of forms of animal life over the earth, or in other ways to add little

[1] In Dean's *Bibliography of Fishes* I count 124 titles by Goode alone, 39 by Goode and Bean, and 14 by Goode and others.

by little to the sum total of our knowledge of natural phenomena, but science, too, needs a synthesis. It must be correlated with the past, and the record of past achievement must be preserved and interpreted for the future. "The history of science is the palladium of its freedom; it prevents it from being tyrannized over by narrow bigoted viewpoints." Goode would have concurred in this motto, which appeared with a lithographed portrait of Ludwig Choulant in 1842; and for the epigraph of one of his essays he quoted Herbert Spencer: "Is not science a growth? Has not science, too, its embryology? And must not the neglect of its embryology lead to a misunderstanding of the principles of its evolution and of its existing organization?" Goode was the man of his generation of American scientists who saw this most clearly.

On January 12, 1887, Goode was made Assistant Secretary of the Smithsonian, with virtually full responsibility for the direction of the National Museum; and in the nine brief years that were left to him he was to bring out (in addition to voluminous other material) six or eight papers on the history of science that were to prove classic. The first of these, "The Beginnings of Natural History in America," he had delivered the previous February as a presidential address before the Biological Society of Washington. Beginning with Thomas Harriot, the earliest English naturalist in America, he traced the development of American natural science to the end of the Revolutionary War, a period of nearly two hundred years, and put on record a mass of historical data indispensable to later historians of science. In a second paper, "The Beginnings of American Science: The Third Century," delivered before the Biological Society in 1887, he carried forward this history to his own day. The next year he read his essay "Museum-History and Museums of History" before the American Historical Association meeting in Washington, which was followed in 1889 by "The Origin of the National Scientific and Educational Institutions of the United States," presented to the same Association. Finally he published three essays which contained his mature ideas and philosophy with respect to museums—"The Museums of the Future," in 1889; "The Genesis of the United States National Museum," in 1893; and "The Principles of Museum Administration," in 1895. The last-mentioned essay was reprinted in South Africa more than fifty years after it first appeared. After Goode's death, all these papers were collected and reprinted in the *Goode Memorial Volume,* published (in 1901) as Part 2 of the *Report* of the National Museum for 1897. This volume, because of Goode's contribution, is one of the most important on the history of American science.

Bibliographer and Collector

GOODE's DEVOTION to science history manifested itself in one other respect—his unusual interest in bibliography. He knew as well as anyone the drudgery connected with the compilation of indexes and bibliographies, yet he realized that they are the necessary tools of the research worker and that there is an obligation laid upon every generation of scientists and scholars to provide works of this character. He would have agreed wholeheartedly with Pope's oft-quoted couplet:

> Index-learning turns no student pale
> Yet holds the eel of science by the tail.

As early as 1874 he began collecting materials for "An Index Bibliography of American Ichthyology," in which he planned to "enumerate by title every writing ever published which refers to American fish or fisheries." This was indeed a gigantic undertaking, and he did not live to see it completed.[2] He inaugurated a series called "Bib-

---

[2] Goode's labors on this index were not wasted, however, for in 1910 when the American zoologist Bashford Dean was compiling his comprehensive *Bibliography of Fishes* the Smithsonian made Goode's index available to him for incorporation in his work. Dean's *Bibliography* was published by the American Museum of Natural History: Vol. 1 in 1916, Vol. 2 in 1917, and Vol. 3 in 1923.

liographies of American Naturalists," several of which were published as bulletins of the National Museum. Three of them—bibliographies of Spencer Fullerton Baird, Charles Girard, and Philip Lutley Sclater—appeared under Goode's name, and he had begun work on two others, those of Theodore Nicholas Gill and David Starr Jordan, both renowned ichthyologists. These bibliographies were no mere trifling lists, but were scholarly, annotated, and well indexed. The one of Baird, published in 1883, alone aggregates nearly four hundred printed pages and still stands as an invaluable source in the study of the career of the Smithsonian's second Secretary.

Goode's interest in history even outside the realm of science was not that of a dilettante. Besides his book on genealogy, *Virginia Cousins,* already mentioned, he wrote "The Literary Labors of Benjamin Franklin," delivered as an address before the American Philosophical Society. He was a member of the council of the American Historical Association and was instrumental in getting through Congress the Act of its incorporation (1889), under which the Association's reports are published by the United States Government. According to law, these reports are transmitted to Congress through the Secretary of the Smithsonian Institution. Goode held membership in the Virginia Historical Society, the Columbia Historical Society, of Washington, and the Southern Historical Society. He helped to organize the Sons of the American Revolution. He assisted, also, in the organization of the Daughters of the American Revolution and designed their seal. Furthermore, he wrote extensively on the history of the Smithsonian itself, and edited and wrote much of the large volume published the year after his death commemorating the fiftieth anniversary of the founding of the Institution.

All these interests and talents added up to make G. Brown Goode the consummate museum director and a godsend to Secretary Baird, who was able to place full trust and responsibility in his assistant secretary. Every museum man ought to have the collecting instinct, and Goode had it to a remarkable and refined degree. But he collected always against the background of his broad museum philosophy, that a museum should not be a mass of collections per se, but "a house full of ideas and a nursery of living thought." And it was not only in his own field of natural history that his genius for collecting displayed itself. "He would," said Langley, "bring back from every exposition which he attended methodical collections, frequently overlooked by others . . . not of miscellaneous objects, but of a series which could themselves be placed on exhibition. These might be musical instruments, ecclesiastical art, early printed books, medals, or ivories," all selected with taste and discrimination. During his regime the number of specimens in the Museum increased from about two hundred thousand to more than three million. This increment might well have resulted in chaos had it not been for Goode's organizing ability and his definite aims for his organization.

Honors and responsibilities came to Goode one after another. He served as commissioner for the United States Government at the International Fisheries Exhibition in Berlin in 1880 and in London in 1883. He represented the Smithsonian at all the great expositions in this country in the decade from 1884 to 1895 and was a commissioner and for a time acting commissioner-general to the Columbia Exposition at Madrid in 1892.

Goode's method of assembling an exhibition, well described by Langley, is revealing: "The plans of the floor space, the cases, the specimens were all carefully arranged in advance. Boxes were especially made of lumber which could be utilized for cases or platforms. Cases were marked, and not very long before the opening of the exposition the entire mass would be deposited on the bare space assigned to the Smithsonian exhibit. Usually other exhibitors had their material half arranged by this time, and the fear was expressed by sympathetic bystanders that the Smithsonian would not be ready. The cases would be unpacked and the specimens put in them in whatever position they happened to stand, and up to the last day all would seem to be in confusion; but Doctor Goode knew his resources and his men as a general knows his army. Suddenly all detailed work would come to an end, and in the course of a few hours, as if by magic, the entire exhibit would be put in place." Goode seemed to take great pride and delight in thus making order out of chaos. He never repeated an exhibition. He received many awards, diplomas, and medals at various expositions, including the Order of Isabella the Catholic from the Spanish Government for his work at the Madrid Exposition.

He served as president of the Biological Society and the Philosophical Society of Washington and was a member of the American Philosophical Society, the National Academy of Sciences, and several foreign scientific societies. He was one of the founders in 1888 of the National Geographic Society, which was to grow in fifty years from a small local scientific organization of two hundred members to a great national institution of more than a million and a half members. He was elected in 1881 a member of the Cosmos Club of Washington and, like his Smithsonian colleagues Baird and Powell, served a term as its president.

Gradually, however, the burden upon Goode's shoulders became more than one man could bear, and though still a young man he broke under the physical strain. All who knew him have remarked how surely he "burned himself out." On September 6, 1896, he died at his home in Washington, at the age of forty-five years; but into those years had been crowded the work of a dozen ordinary men. With his death a golden age of natural history came to an end. There were, of course, many of the old-time naturalists still alive, but the age of acute specialization in science had set in, and perhaps never again could there be a man like George Brown Goode. He was, as the magazine *Science* said in its simple announcement of his death, "one of the ablest and best men in America."

He was buried in Oak Hill Cemetery in Georgetown, D. C., not far from the tomb of Joseph Henry and that of his mentor, Spencer Fullerton Baird. Today his unmarked grave may be found on inquiry from the caretaker; but perhaps he needs no other monument than the solid and enduring part he played in guiding the destiny of the Smithsonian Institution and its ward, the National Museum.

"Bairdians"

STRONG as Goode was in the antiquarian and educational aspects of museum work, he was just as able and anxious to foster the research activities, which were a part of his threefold plan for an ideal museum. Being a zoologist himself, he fully understood the research problems and needs in this field. He was interested no little, too, in anthropology, and one colleague said of him, "It would be difficult to find among those who are professional anthropologists a man who had a more exalted idea of what this science ought to be." And it was during the time of Baird and Goode that there came to the scientific staff of the Museum a number of leaders of American natural history who were to work under them. These were the "Bairdians" mentioned at the beginning of this chapter. Among them Elliott Coues (1842-99), a brilliant student of zoology who worked chiefly on a collaborating basis, was early in the front rank of ornithologists, and, with Thomas M. Brewer and Baird, helped to produce an outstanding *History of North American Birds.* Alone he produced numerous and voluminous works on exploration and natural science. There was also William Healey Dall (1845-1927), member of the Kennicott Alaska Expedition, who served many years with the United States Geological Survey, and was for fifty-nine years (1868-1927) also honorary curator of the Division of Mollusks and Tertiary Fossils in the Museum; he contributed in many other

PLATE 23.   The Freer Gallery of Art

PLATE 24.   Charles Doolittle Walcott, fourth secretary of the Smithsonian
Institution, 1907-1927

ways to the Museum's scientific work in conchology, and became the biographer of Baird. There was William Henry Holmes (1846-1933), geologist, archeologist, and artist. Leonhard Stejneger (1851-1943), the Norwegian-born biologist, spent a lifetime at the Smithsonian and distinguished himself both as an ornithologist and as a herpetologist.

There were many others whose stories are a part of the history of the Smithsonian. They worked behind the scenes, perhaps world-renowned specialists in their fields. Without them the National Museum and the Smithsonian would have languished scientifically. A "thumbnail" sketch of one of these may suffice to show the kind of "curator" that was typical of the Baird-Goode period.

This man was Robert Ridgway (1850-1929), who was to follow in Baird's footsteps as the foremost ornithologist of his day. He began corresponding with Baird when he was only fourteen years old, a boy at Mount Carmel, Illinois, and in 1867, when he was seventeen, through Baird's influence he was appointed as a zoologist under Clarence King to assist in the geological survey of the Fortieth Parallel. At nineteen he published his first paper on birds —a note on the belted kingfisher, which appeared in 1869 in the *American Naturalist*. The same year the Academy of Natural Sciences of Philadelphia published his "Notices of Certain Obscurely Known Species of American Birds." These papers were the beginning of Ridgway's hundreds of contributions to ornithology, extending over a period of sixty years. His official connection with the Smithsonian began in 1874, and from then until his death in 1929 he served as the Museum's chief ornithologist, his title changing from time to time, from simply "ornithologist" to "curator of birds."

Ridgway's most pretentious work, which is probably the most ambitious undertaking in American systematic ornithology, was *The Birds of North and Middle America*. This catalogue, which includes technical descriptions of every form of bird known from the northern section of the Western Hemisphere, with complete synonymies, identification keys, ranges, seasonal plumages, diagnostic characters, and measurements, consumed most of his official time from 1894 until his death thirty-five years later. Eight volumes were published by the National Museum during his lifetime, two have appeared posthumously, and the series is being completed by his successor.

Both Robert Ridgway and his younger brother, John, were considerably talented as painters of bird portraits, and they executed drawings for the color plates of such distinguished books as Albert Kenrick Fisher's *Hawks and Owls of the United States.* As a boy, Robert had mixed his own paints in his father's drugstore in Illinois, and he soon became deeply interested in the subject of color. He early saw the need, especially for the use of naturalists who must be able to describe species of plants and animals with unmistakable accuracy, for a standardization of colors and color terms. To this problem he devoted his serious attention, and in 1886 he was able to bring out his first work on the subject—*A Nomenclature of Color for Naturalists.* In this he presented ten plates showing 186 named colors in small rectangles. The value of the work was apparent to all concerned, and its reception encouraged him to continue his color studies. Twenty-five years passed, however, before he was ready with the new and enlarged edition of his color manual. In this book, *Color Standards and Color Nomenclature,* were illustrated 1,115 named colors, for which he had scientifically mixed the pigments himself according to standard proportions which he had worked out; these specifications appeared in the book in tabular form. *Color Standards* became widely used not only by naturalists but also by paint manufacturers, chemists, florists, and artists. It found many commercial and industrial uses, and although other and more modern color standards have since been published, Ridgway's was a pioneer work and has never been entirely superseded. Among naturalists it is still the "color bible." It made Ridgway's name known far outside of

ornithological circles and constituted perhaps his most important contribution to science.

Baird, Goode, Coues, Ridgway, Dall, Stejneger—these
were a few of the naturalists who helped make the Smithsonian great during its first half century. Elsewhere [3] I
have paid tribute to their kind and their influence in a
way I should like to repeat here:

> The sons of science walk in endless line
> Bearing the torch; a few falter and drop,
> But the rest close in: they who have glimpsed a sign
> Far on ahead that reads, "You must not stop!"
> Their quests are strange and wonderful—to bring
> The stars to earth, to take the earth to sky;
> To know the *what* of every living thing
> Of all time past, and then the *how* and *why*.
> And here is one whose vision has been long
> And clear and true—he saw the sign ahead.
> His torch was radiant, and he held it strong;
> Where it found darkness there came light instead . . .
> Forever seeking truth, not vain acclaims,
> He kindled, on the way, a thousand other flames.

[3] A sonnet written on the occasion of the ninetieth birthday of Leonhard Stejneger (*Science,* October 31, 1941).

7

SAMUEL PIERPONT LANGLEY

ON THE same day, January 12, 1887, that George Brown Goode was appointed Assistant Secretary of the Smithsonian Institution to direct the affairs of the National Museum, another Assistant Secretary was appointed to lighten still further the administrative burden on Professor Baird's shoulders. Ten months later this man—Samuel Pierpont Langley—became the third Secretary of the Institution. In the eighteen years that he held the office, he gained distinction both for himself and for the Smithsonian; during his service he achieved notice in several branches of scientific research. He was an original thinker, with supreme "faith in the truth that makes mankind free." His administration was marked by definite progress, for he was not a man who stood still. He possessed an indomitable perseverance that is remarked upon by all who knew him. James Smithson would have been proud of him.

Like Joseph Henry before him, Langley had already attained a distinguished reputation as a scientist before he came to the Smithsonian. He was internationally known as an astronomer, having spent twenty years as director of the Allegheny Observatory, near Pittsburgh, and professor of physics at Western University of Pennsylvania, and was recognized to be in the front rank of American astronomers, along with such men as Simon Newcomb, Charles E. Young, and Edward C. Pickering. He never married, and free of family ties and responsibilities, he devoted his life to science. He is remembered for his contributions to the science of astrophysics and to aeronautics. Furthermore, he was a great Secretary, with abilities equal to those of his predecessors.

Langley was born on August 22, 1834, at Roxbury, Mass., which is now a part of Boston. He was born and bred thoroughly New England. Among his ancestors were Increase and Cotton Mather; his great-grandfather was a Revolutionary soldier who helped suppress Shays's Rebellion. He attended the Boston Latin School and in 1850 was graduated from the Boston English High School; but he was not sent to college, probably because his talent lay along mechanical lines, which did not seem to require college training, and because his chief interest was astronomy, which was not then to be taken seriously as a career in which to make one's living.

The Astronomer

LANGLEY'S FATHER was a wholesale merchant with no recorded interest in science, but at least he did not discourage this interest in his sons. We are told that young Samuel and his brother John had a small telescope through which they watched the building of Bunker Hill Monument. This structure on Breeds Hill was completed in 1843 before Samuel was nine years old. Years later Langley wrote, "I cannot remember when I was not interested in astronomy. I remember reading books upon the subject as early as nine, and when I was quite a boy I learned to make little telescopes, and studied the stars through them. Later I made some larger ones . . . and

111

I think myself they were very good for a boy. One of the most wonderful things to me was the sun. . . . I used to hold my hands up to it and wonder how the rays made them warm, and where the heat came from and how."

Anxious to put his mechanical and mathematical abilities and his unusual deftness with tools to some use, young Langley began the study of civil engineering and architecture. By the time he was twenty-three, in 1857, he felt equipped to start out on his own, and for the next seven years he was moderately successful as an architect, practicing mainly in St. Louis and Chicago. Luckily for science, however, he decided to abandon his profession, and in 1864 he returned to Boston to resume his study of astronomy. His brother John had just returned from three years' service as a naval surgeon, and with nothing better to do at the moment the two of them decided to build a reflecting telescope. John, who became professor of physics at the University of Michigan and later was connected with the Case School of Applied Sciences in Cleveland, has recorded something of this event:

We had about three months in which both of us were free from fixed duties. . . . My brother and I had made the acquaintance of Alvan Clark, Sr., who at that time was a portrait painter. He had a studio in Tremont Street, Boston, but he was just abandoning art for optics, and his studio contained about as many lenses in an unfinished state as it did portraits, also incomplete. At this time the Smithsonian Institution had recently published a monograph by the younger Draper, of New York, on the making of a reflecting telescope. This, and the advice of Mr. Clark, were all we had to go upon. We had a small foot-lathe and a few tools in the barn belonging to the house where we were living, and with this outfit we undertook to make a reflecting telescope seven inches in diameter by five feet in focal length, all the work on which, both optical and mechanical, was to be made with our own hands, and nothing but crude material and a few necessary tools were to be purchased. Above all things, no lenses or other complete optical apparatus were on any account to be bought; we were to make it all.

The telescope was built, although it took all the brothers' spare time for nearly three years. "Success was finally reached," wrote John, "the instrument showing practically perfect definition for one of its type and style; but probably the finished reflector represented at least twenty others abandoned or reground before this result was reached."

This was to prove a valuable experience for the young astronomer. After a year spent in Europe with his brother —studying languages, visiting art collections, and sightseeing—Samuel returned to New England in the fall of 1865 to learn that the observatory at Cambridge was seeking assistants. Apparently not much persuasion was needed to convince the director that young Langley should be one of these, and thus his brilliant career as a professional astronomer began. The next year, following the end of the Civil War, he accepted the post of assistant professor of mathematics in the United States Naval Academy at Annapolis, where he reorganized and rejuvenated the small observatory. The following year he was asked to become director of the Allegheny Observatory and professor of astronomy and physics in the Western University of Pennsylvania. When it is remembered that he lacked a college education, we must marvel at his rapid rise in the world of science. He stayed at Pittsburgh twenty years and attained high eminence and reputation.

During his early days at the Allegheny Observatory Langley made a contribution to the technique of time-keeping that, if he had never done anything else, would have caused him to be remembered. Up to that time only scattered attempts had been made to standardize time by means of telegraphic transmission of time signals. Travelers, especially those by rail, were perpetually annoyed by the disparity of clocks between one station and the next. Watches and clocks were set by other watches and clocks, with results that were frequently anything but accurate or convenient. Langley thought of a scheme to correct this state of affairs, and in 1869 he made a proposal for regulating the clocks of the Pennsylvania Central Railway and other railroads associated with it. The Pennsylvania System then comprised over twenty-five hundred miles of railroad east and west of Pittsburgh, with more than three hundred telegraph stations. The next year his system was inaugurated, and accurate signals based on solar time were sent twice a day to each of these offices from the Allegheny Observatory. Eventually about eight thousand miles of railroad were run by this one clock, and the correct time was thus made accessible to virtually every inhabitant. Incidentally, the income that resulted from the operation of this system was used by Langley in building up the impoverished Allegheny Observatory, and it soon compared favorably with other observatories in facilities and apparatus.

Langley's time system, then, was the parent of the standard-time transmission system of today. Even if it was not, as Dr. Cyrus Adler has said, "an important advance in knowledge, it must be counted a really great contribution to the convenience, comfort, and welfare of mankind." Certainly few scientists have applied their ingenuity more usefully.

The year 1869 saw the publication of Langley's first scientific paper, which was a brief account of his observations at Oakland, Ky., of the 1869 eclipse of the sun. In Spain the next year he watched another solar eclipse and made important observations upon the sun's coronal rays. This was the beginning of many years of research by him upon the solar atmosphere. In 1873 he completed his telescope study of the sun's face and at the Portland meeting of the American Association for the Advancement of Science that year exhibited his constructed picture of "a typical sunspot," based on three years of study. Years later his drawings were still found to be remarkably accurate, and it was said that they gave "a better idea of the minute surface of the sun than is afforded by the best photographs."

His scientific treatises were composed with the greatest

care. Typical was his early paper on "The Minute Structure of the Solar Photosphere," concerning which one of his American colleagues in astronomy, Edward Singleton Holden, wrote, "It possesses that hardly definable quality by which we become aware that it was written from a full mind. It is only fifteen pages long, yet we are not conscious of undue brevity. One has a sense in reading that every statement of fact, or every expression of opinion, is based upon a hundred concurring judgments." Much later, in the year of the Langley Centennial (1934), Dr. C. G. Abbot wrote: "As an author he showed great clarity of expression and delightful rhythm and choice of words. He could never satisfy his fastidious taste in composition, but continually altered and polished his writings up to the very last stage. Only in bound form could they elude his further alterations."

During Langley's later years at the Allegheny Observatory he was able to do considerable popular writing and lecturing. Some of the lectures later appeared in *Century Magazine* and still later (1888) were collected in his book *The New Astronomy,* which "passed through several editions and became a classic in astronomical literature."

Instrument-Maker

ASTRONOMY, the oldest of the sciences, has never lacked American devotees. Its possibilities are so unlimited that it challenges the imaginations of countless amateurs as well as of the professional investigators whose discoveries add to the sum-total of astronomical knowledge. More, perhaps, than in any other science, advancement depends upon the concurrent development of new and improved instruments; in this field American ingenuity has excelled, as the 200-inch telescope in California today attests.

About 1850 the president of the Royal Astronomical Society said, "The Americans of the United States, although late in the field of astronomical enterprise, have now taken up that science with their characteristic energy, and have already shown their ability to instruct their former masters." Perhaps the greatest of the telescope builders was Alvan Clark, whose studio in Boston the Langley brothers frequented. In 1860 Clark made the 18-inch telescope for the Dearborn Observatory at Evanston, Ill.; in 1872 he built the 26-incher for the United States Naval Observatory in Washington; and in 1886 his shops produced the 36-inch telescope for the Lick Observatory in California. These progressive achievements were accompanied in each case by signal astronomical discoveries —the doubleness of the star Sirius, the moon of Mars, the rings of Saturn, etc.—and stimulated astronomers to demand bigger and better instruments. Clark died in 1887. One of his successors was John A. Brashear, a friend of Langley. Under Langley's encouragement Brashear, a steel worker, was "transformed from a timid amateur mirror-grinder to the founder of that great optical concern, the John A. Brashear Optical Company, of Allegheny, Pa."

Langley himself had a genius for instrument-making, and when about 1870 he turned his attention to the study of the heat of the sun he found it necessary to devise a new type of thermometer. His early work in this field had been done by aid of a thermopile, an instrument long used in determining slight differences in temperature but not sensitive or trustworthy enough for Langley's purposes. With it he had measured the heat from various parts of the sun's disk and, following Joseph Henry's observations of half a century earlier, studied the effect of sunspots on our climates. The thermopile of that day was not capable, however, of measuring the minute amount of heat distributed in a heat-spectrum, though recently it has become a leading instrument for such work.

Langley, therefore, devised a new instrument, which he called the bolometer, or actinic balance, and which he announced to the scientific world at a meeting of the American Academy of Arts and Sciences at Boston in January 1881. The bolometer is an extremely delicate kind of thermometer, whose action is based on "variation of electrical resistance produced by changes of temperature in a metallic conductor." This metallic conductor is a thin strip of blackened platinum forming one arm of an electric balance, and when exposed even to the infinitesimal amount of radiant heat given off by a spectrum it is sensitized and the heat may be registered by a delicate galvanometer. The instrument is remarkable for (1) its precision, or the degree of exactitude with which it can be set on a special point, such as a line of the spectrum; (2) its accuracy, or its ability to repeat the same measurement of radiation under like conditions; and (3) its sensitiveness. In 1898 Langley claimed that his bolometric apparatus would indicate a change of temperature in its strips of "much less than one-ten-millionth of a degree centigrade." His instrument not only indicated, it actually measured radiant energy.

The bolometer opened a new era in astrophysics and made possible many important discoveries pertaining to solar radiation. Utilizing it in studies of the solar spectrum, Langley was able to demonstrate that the maximum of heat is in the orange portion of the normal spectrum, and to explore and locate completely new portions of the infrared spectrum. The heat of sunspots and of various parts of the sun's disk, and the temperature of the moon, were subjected to his measurements. Absorption of the sun's rays by the earth's atmosphere was studied. He showed that the sun's disk radiates 5,300 times as much light and 87 times as much heat as would an equal area of metal in a Bessemer furnace going full blast. The firefly, he pointed out, is unique in being able to convert all its heat into light, in contrast to the gas flame, which utilizes only 2 per cent of its heat.

This research was pioneering in science to an extraordinary degree and was building up for Langley an eminence that perhaps he himself would have discredited. As one member of the Smithsonian Board of Regents later remarked, "The thoroughness, ingenuity, and beauty of his methods and the clearness of his style in presenting them attracted attention far and wide." It is little wonder, then, that the name of Samuel P. Langley was at the top when, early in 1887, Secretary Baird was faced with the problem of selecting a new Assistant Secretary.

Director of the Smithsonian Observatory

ALTHOUGH HIS YEARS at Allegheny Observatory had been scientifically productive, they had been lonely ones for Langley. Pittsburgh did not seem to supply the companionship that his intellect craved. He was interested in literature and art and philosophy, as well as science, and of a Sunday evening he would "navigate" Observatory Hill specifically to spend a few hours in the backroom of a certain drugstore, where "four or five men would assemble to discuss the great things of the mind and the scientific problems of the day." So it was not, as Cyrus Adler has pointed out, professional ambition that brought him to Washington on Baird's invitation, but "principally the desire to associate with others of his own kind." Langley wrote to Baird: "Both professional and domestic life here are exceptionally isolated, and I have felt the need of some change which would bring with it, along with society, new occupation, if that could be of a kind not wholly dissociated from my accustomed pursuits."

Baird did not intend for Langley to give up his astronomical research for administrative duties as Assistant Secretary; rather, he wanted the Institution to aid this research in every way possible and eventually to build up the Smithsonian's own facilities for work along the lines of Langley's interests. Baird felt, too, that perhaps the activities of the Institution were becoming unbalanced in favor of natural history and that it was time to start the pendulum swinging again toward the physical sciences, which had been nearest the heart of Joseph Henry. During the discussion concerning disposal of the Smithson bequest, John Quincy Adams had advocated establishing an observatory, and now Baird rejuvenated the idea. Although the Regents accepted his plan for an astrophysical observatory, specializing in the "new astronomy" in which Langley had pioneered, Baird did not live to see it fulfilled. Langley, naturally, anxiously and actively promoted the project, and the establishment of the Smithsonian's Astrophysical Observatory was one of the first achievements of his secretaryship.

The Observatory began in 1890 in a modest way in a wooden structure erected by the Institution south of the Smithsonian Building. At the outset it received financial support from two friends of the Institution—Jerome H. Kidder and Alexander Graham Bell—who each contributed $5,000. Government support of the Observatory began the next year with an appropriation of $10,000, support which has continued to the present time. As long as Langley lived, he was the mentor and inspiration of the Observatory. Today, as then, it is conducting original research in astrophysics that is duplicated nowhere else in the world.

In contrast to the purpose of the usual astronomical observatory—"to study the places and motions of the heavenly bodies, with little special reference to the wants of man in his daily life"—the purpose of the Astrophysical Observatory, said Langley, was to find out how the sun "affects the earth and the wants of man on it: how its heat is distributed, and how it, in fact, affects not only the seasons and the farmer's crops, but the whole system of living things on the earth." The early work of the Observatory has been summed up by Dr. C. G. Abbot, Langley's assistant who later became Secretary:

Its first contribution was the bolographic scanning of the infrared solar spectrum to map the lines and bands of absorption there [beyond those that could be discerned by spectrophotography]. These lines and bands are caused by the gases of the sun's and earth's atmosphere. In doing this, the hairlike bolometer, which had been an untamed instrument, became easier to use than a mercury thermometer, though capable of measuring temperatures of less than a millionth of a degree. The research . . . showed the distribution of intensities in the solar spectrum from 0.76 to 5.3 microns of wave length. It disclosed 740 lines and bands of absorption in this region and indicated their relative intensities. It included a precise determination of the dispersion of rock salt and of fluorite, materials much used for infrared spectroscopy.

Another problem which received study was the determination of the proportion of the sun's heat that actually reached the earth and the amount dispersed in the outer atmosphere. Langley undertook to find out more accurately than was previously known the solar constant of radiation, i.e., the amount of solar heat before it enters the atmosphere of the earth. Another question to be answered was: Is the sun a variable star, and, if so, how do its variations affect the weather? Langley and his assistants, notably Dr. Abbot and Frederick E. Fowle, attacked these problems with the aid of the facilities set up at the Observatory, modest though they were.

Accomplishments of the Observatory

THESE RESEARCHES, most of them tracing back to the invention and perfection of the bolometer by Langley, have continued through the years, and in 1946 Dr. Abbot [1] listed sixteen principal results and accomplishments. These are so important in showing the fundamental type of science stemming from Langley's secretaryship that they are here enumerated:

(1) The solar constant of radiation was found to lie within 1 per cent of 1.94 calories per centimeter square per minute. This was checked spectrobolometrically by sounding balloon observations at an altitude of 15 miles.

(2) The sun was found to be a variable star, subject to changes of output, never as yet observed to exceed 5 per cent and usually less than 1 per cent.

1 *Science*, vol. 104, p. 118.

(3) The sun's variations were found to be of two types: day-to-day changes; and long-interval solar-radiation changes of a cyclic nature, 16 of which go simultaneously, with periods ranging from 7 to 273 months.

(4) Both day-to-day and long periodic solar changes were found to affect the weather.

(5) The atmospheric transmission for radiation was measured at over 40 wave lengths under a great variety of conditions.

(6) The amount of radiation scattered by sky and clouds was measured.

(7) The distribution of radiation over the sun's disk was determined for many wave lengths.

(8) The temperature of the sun was found to be about 6,000° Absolute Centigrade.

(9) The energy spectrum curve of solar radiation was determined between wave lengths 0.34 and 2.35 microns.

(10) The change of form of the energy spectrum curve attending solar variation was determined and found to be rapidly increasing toward short wave lengths for increasing values of the solar constant.

(11) Solar energy was harnessed for power, distilling, and cooking, with an efficiency of power production of over 20 per cent obtained.

(12) Transmission of long-wave radiation through long columns of air containing known loads of water vapor and carbon dioxide was studied.

(13) The amount of ozone in the atmosphere was computed with high accuracy.

(14) The reflecting power, or albedo, of an infinitely extending cloud surface was measured.

(15) Radiometric determinations were made with the 100-inch telescope at Mount Wilson, Calif., of the distribution of radiation in the spectra of twenty bright stars and planets.

(16) Standard instruments for measuring sun and sky radiation were devised, used, and furnished abroad to fix the scale of measurement of solar radiation in heat units.

National Zoological Park

ANOTHER AGENCY that came into being under the Smithsonian during Langley's regime was the National Zoological Park; it originated and developed under his personal guidance. In the National Museum a department of living animals had been created, chiefly for the use of the taxidermists who wished to have live animals to study. Heading this department was William Temple Hornaday, then a skillful taxidermist and ardent explorer, but who in later years became a zealous conservationist and head of the New York Zoological Park. By 1888 his department at the Museum had about 225 living animals to care for.

About this time the American bison, or buffalo, made its last stand against the wanton destruction by hunters. Only a few scattered herds of these magnificent mammals remained, and Hornaday attempted to arouse public interest in preserving what was left of them. Furthermore, the fate of the buffalo, he thought, should be a sad object lesson, and in the National Museum *Annual Report* for 1886-87 appeared his noted work *The Extermination of the American Bison,* which in addition to being a valuable natural-history document, focused public attention toward the need of conserving other American species of big game. Hornaday's "zoo" contained six captive buffaloes, and both he and Langley believed that if this "herd" could be increased and exhibited in Washington the educational work in conservation would be greatly furthered.[2]

Langley proceeded, therefore, to bring the matter before Congress. He and Hornaday had already made a survey of possible sites for such a "zoological garden" in the Capital City and agreed that the valley of Rock Creek, with its woods and waters, rocky cliffs, picturesque hillsides, and other attractive features, would make an ideal location and would be well adapted for wild animals. Selection of this

[2] The term "conservation," however, as applied to natural resources did not come into use until the time of Theodore Roosevelt and Gifford Pinchot.

site proved to be a masterly choice, considered from the viewpoint of the welfare of the City of Washington, for the whole area later became Rock Creek Park, a magnificent little "wilderness" in the heart of the city, with the Zoo nestled in one corner.

The idea of a national zoo gradually won the lawmakers. After the usual amount of cogitation and debate in Congress, the National Zoological Park was established and in 1890 was placed under the direction of the Smithsonian Institution; an appropriation of $200,000 was made for the purchase of land, and a commission was appointed to select and obtain the site. Mr. Hornaday became the first superintendent, but he resigned at the end of a year, to be succeeded by Dr. Frank Baker, who served for many years. Of the Zoo W. P. True, Smithsonian editor, has written:

With rare foresight, Secretary Langley, instead of proceeding to develop the new National Zoological Park piecemeal with the limited funds available at the start, interested a world-renowned landscape architect, Frederick Law Olmsted, in drawing up a comprehensive plan for the entire future of the project as a whole. With the orderly growth of the Park thus assured, a central area of fifty acres was selected for immediate occupancy, the rest being left in its state of unspoiled natural beauty. The necessary roads were constructed, the grounds were cleared and improved, and one animal house— all that could be attempted with the money available—was constructed. In a borrowed wagon, all the animals that had been kept in sheds back of the Smithsonian—some 185 strong —made the journey to their new home, and the National Zoological Park was opened to the public.

Today, after sixty years of expansion and growth, the National Zoo is one of the best in the world, and more than two and a half million visitors enter its gates every year. No one can well deny that, under the Smithsonian's direction, it has been a notable means of diffusing zoological knowledge.

Langley himself was fond of visiting the Zoo, for he

liked to get away from crowds of people. (In Langley's day, strange as it seems to us, a person *could* avoid the crowds by going to the zoo.) During the time when he was beginning his aeronautical studies, he would watch and photograph the flight of vultures and other birds from a specially built platform in an oak tree in the Park, and then retreat to one of the quiet Zoo offices to work out his calculations.

A National Gallery of Art

IN SPITE OF THE companionship he found in associating with his scientific colleagues, Langley because of his innate aloofness was essentially a lonely man. Today we should probably call him an introvert, perhaps seeking to conceal his introversion with an air of brusqueness. He was well aware of this trait, and could even joke about his capacity for silence. Cyrus Adler, Assistant Secretary under Langley, tells in his autobiography of going with him on long, cold, winter carriage drives in Washington: "We could both be silent for hours, and thus established a friendship which was free from dialectics. . . . As a young man he was a worshipper of Thomas Carlyle, and summer after summer went to England and had the privilege of sitting in a corner of Carlyle's library and hearing the great man talk. One day Carlyle invited him out for a drive, and they were together nearly four hours. The next day, a friend met Langley and said to him: 'Carlyle paid you a great compliment. He said you were the most sensible American he had ever met.' To which Langley responded: 'Yes, I was with him for four hours and never opened my mouth.' "

Like his colleague George Brown Goode, Langley was a man of wide interests in matters outside the realm of science. In literature and art his taste was discriminating. Among his favorites in the world of letters was the English traveler and linguist George Borrow, author of *Lavengro, The Bible in Spain,* and *The Romany Rye,* and he owned some of Borrow's original manuscripts. He was fond of Heinrich Heine, the German lyric poet. The American novelist William Dean Howells was his friend, and it is recorded that he even took lessons in composition from this renowned stylist. He delved deep into English and French history and had a passion for the memoirs of the great figures; it is said that he read everything he could find on Leonardo da Vinci, Oliver Cromwell, Frederick the Great, Louis XIV, Napoleon, and Abraham Lincoln. He strove to look out upon life with a truly catholic spirit, so that nothing human would be foreign to him. This outlook was reflected in his choice of one of his assistant secretaries, Dr. Cyrus Adler, who represented the humanities rather than the natural or physical sciences.

Langley's interest in art was keen, and it must have been a source of great satisfaction to him that he was able to bring about during his administration the formal creation of a National Gallery of Art under the Smithsonian. Objects of art, of course, had been coming to the Institution since its very begining. A gallery of art, in fact, had been one of the organizers' desires. But art had never been more than a sideline. As we have seen, the fire in the Smithsonian Building in 1865 destroyed much valuable art material, and thereafter, for about thirty years, most of the paintings, prints, and other art objects received by the Institution were turned over to the Library of Congress and to the Corcoran Gallery of Art in Washington. After the Centennial Exhibition of 1876 in Philadelphia, which yielded a hundred carloads of collections of all kinds for the National Museum and resulted in the erection of a new Museum building in 1881, interest in developing the art collections was renewed. In 1896 the material that had been deposited in the Corcoran Gallery and the Library of Congress was recalled, and a large room in the eastern wing of the Smithsonian Building was fitted up for prints and an art library.

The matter was brought to a culmination and the art collections of the Institution were given a formal standing and name by a bequest of paintings from Mrs. Harriet Lane Johnston, the niece of James Buchanan. While Buchanan was President, just before the Civil War, Mrs. Johnston had been mistress of the White House, and she had accompanied her uncle when he was minister to England. Interested in art, she had collected at her home in Washington an assemblage of paintings and other historical objects of some value. When she died in 1903 it was found that she had left this entire collection to the Corcoran Gallery of Art, with the stipulation that should the United States Government ever establish in Washington a national gallery of art the collection should be turned over to it and become its absolute property. Under these conditions the Corcoran Gallery declined the bequest, with the result that the next year by a court decree the art collections of the Smithsonian Institution were "designated and established" as the National Gallery of Art. Following about two years of litigation, the Harriet Lane Johnston collection, thirty-one pieces in all (paintings, marbles, and miscellaneous articles), was delivered to the Smithsonian Building and installed in the reception room and Secretary's office. Later a temporary picture gallery was provided in the Museum Building. Represented among the paintings were works by John Constable, Sir Thomas Lawrence, Bernardino Luini, Sir Joshua Reynolds, and George Romney.

The United States of America had then at last a National Gallery of Art. Though it reached its greatest development after his day, nevertheless it was Langley who nurtured it in its infancy, and in 1906, the year that he died, the Gallery received [3] another gift which demonstrated its great value as a national depository. This was the collection of American and Oriental art presented by Charles L. Freer, of Detroit. This generous gift included some 2,250 art objects—among them paintings by James McNeill Whistler, Dwight W. Tryon, Thomas W. Dew-

[3] The Freer gift was offered and accepted during Langley's life, but formal transfer did not occur until later.

ing, and Abbott H. Thayer, and a wealth of Japanese and Chinese pottery, bronzes, sculpture, manuscripts, and paintings of great value. The bequest further provided for the erection of a separate building to house the collection. Under the name Freer Gallery of Art this building was opened to the public in 1923. Built in the style of a Florentine Renaissance palace, it forms one of the more impressive structures of the Capital City. "My great desire," said Mr. Freer, "has been to unite modern work with masterpieces of certain periods of high civilization in spiritual and physical suggestion, having the power to broaden esthetic culture and the grace to elevate the human mind." This, too, seems in keeping with the ideals of James Smithson.

In the years since Freer's gift other priceless collections have been added to the National Gallery, through the gifts or bequests of such men as William T. Evans, Henry Ward Ranger, Ralph Cross Johnson, and John Gellatly. Then, in 1937, Andrew W. Mellon gave to the people of the United States through the Smithsonian his huge art collection and a $15,000,000 building. The name National Gallery of Art was transferred to the "Mellon Gallery," and a new name, National Collection of Fine Arts, was given to the collections that had been known as the National Gallery of Art. But the story of the new National Gallery of Art is something else again. It is something of which Langley could little have dreamed.

International Catalogue of Scientific Literature

ANOTHER VENTURE to which Langley lent a guiding hand was the *International Catalogue of Scientific Literature*—nurtured by the Smithsonian Institution for nearly three decades. The idea of such a catalogue originated with Secretary Joseph Henry, for it was he who proposed to the Royal Society of London the desirability of publishing some kind of cooperative catalogue of scientific literature. Acting upon his suggestion, the Society, beginning in 1867, published a general catalogue of scientific papers, which has become a desideratum for every important library in the world. Finally, however, this became too burdensome and expensive for the Society to continue.

Scientists the world over realized that some sort of continuing guide and index to their publications was badly needed. In all fields of research so many scientific books, memoirs, papers, and articles appeared every year that it was well-nigh impossible for a specialist to keep abreast of the literature being published. Two international conferences on the problem were held, but no agreement could be reached. A third meeting, convened at London in June 1900, resulted in the formal establishment of the *International Catalogue*. It was decided that each country participating in the scheme should catalogue the current literature in pure science published within its boundaries and that the catalogue cards should be sent to London, there to be assembled and published in seventeen annual volumes under the following subjects: Mathematics, Mechanics, Physics, Chemistry, Astronomy, Meteorology, Mineralogy, Geology, Geography, Paleontology, General Biology, Botany, Zoology, Human Anatomy, Physical Anthropology, Physiology, and Bacteriology.

These seventeen annual volumes (about 250 in all) were published from 1901 to 1915. Libraries, colleges, and other institutions, besides several private individuals in the United States, subscribed to the catalogue. The Library of Congress subscribed to three complete sets, one of them printed on one side of the page only, on thin paper, to be cut up and transferred to cards.

It was a gigantic undertaking. At the beginning, funds to carry on the work of cataloguing the American science literature seemed to be unavailable, and for about five years the Smithsonian did its best to keep the project moving, but with very insufficient money to devote to it. In 1906, however, Congress came to the rescue and appropriated $5,000 for the Regional Bureau of the *Inter-*

national Catalogue of Scientific Literature under the Smithsonian. Congressional support was continued for nine years, until the outbreak of World War I disrupted the whole organization. Some countries (notably France) published their part of the *Catalogue* separately for a time, and the United States Regional Bureau continued its work in manuscript for several years, until finally Congressional appropriations for the work ceased.

The *International Catalogue* was a notable experiment in international cooperation. It filled a definite need that since its demise has been met in part piecemeal by individual groups (such as the *Zoological Record, Chemical Abstracts,* and *Biological Abstracts*). It is the hope of some that this idea of Joseph Henry's, so valiantly aided by Samuel P. Langley and his associates at the Smithsonian, will some day be revived, perhaps by the United Nations, UNESCO, or other internationally and scientifically minded agency. But it may be that the sum total of even pure-science literature has outgrown the bounds of a single catalogue scheme, and that some new technique of the cataloguer's art must be developed before this "eel of science" can successfully be held by the tail.

Pioneer in Aeronautics

WHEN HE CAME to the Smithsonian Institution, Samuel P. Langley brought with him an interest in aeronautics that equaled his concern with astronomy. His relentless pursuit of this study was to bring him both fame and disappointment. Whether he built the first airplane "capable of sustained free flight with a man" is a question which perhaps is not likely ever to be finally answered. We are not here greatly concerned with the details of that controversy, but rather with Langley's basic scientific contributions to aeronautics and the part which the Smithsonian played in aiding them.

The Institution's interest in aeronautics dates almost from the beginning of its work. It pioneered in meteorological research and conducted studies on the nature of the atmosphere. In 1860 it was asked to aid Thaddeus Lowe in experiments to cross the Atlantic by balloon,[4] and the next year Secretary Henry took an active interest in Lowe's important balloon experiments in Washington. In the Smithsonian Annual *Report* for 1863 appeared two articles on aeronautical subjects: a translation of a paper by James Smithson's friend Arago, "Aeronautical Voyages Performed with a View to the Advancement of Science," and an account of the balloon ascensions of James Glaisher, British aeronaut. Thereafter, through eight and a half decades, aeronautics has been high among Smithsonian interests. But Langley was its greatest protagonist.

He began his aviation studies while still at the Allegheny Observatory. Since boyhood he had been intrigued by the mysterious power of flight possessed by birds and would watch with wonder the graceful motions of buzzards and hawks flying overhead. In 1886, equipped with a scientist's curiosity and a genius for designing instruments, he began to think seriously about the problem and soon concluded that the prevailing theories as to how birds fly were unsound. To answer the question rightly was a tremendous challenge to him. He knew that to fly had been man's dream since history began, and that man's attempts thus far had met with but limited success and even derision.

Courageously he started his first experiments and observations in aerodynamics. By means of a large whirling table and other ingenious automatic instruments he studied the lift and resistance of rapidly moving surfaces in air; this work he continued after he was called to Washington. In 1891 the Smithsonian published the results of his studies under the title *Experiments in Aerodynamics* in its *Contributions to Knowledge* series, and his con-

[4] No financial assistance was given—only a letter of "advice" from Professor Henry.

clusions immediately attracted world-wide attention among physicists.

One of his conclusions was that "so far as the mere power to sustain heavy bodies in the air by mechanical flight goes, such mechanical flight is possible with engines we now possess." The distinguished engineer Octave Chanute remarked (in 1896): "It is significant that prior to the publication of Doctor Langley's work, it was the rare exception to find engineers and scientists of recognized ability who would fully admit the *possibility* of man being able to solve the twenty-century old problem of aviation." But now, he said, "it is the exception to find an intelligent engineer who disputes the *probability* of the eventual solution of the problem of man-flight. Such has been the change in five years. Incredulity has given way, interest has been aroused in the scientific question, a sound basis has been furnished for experiment, and practical results are being evolved by many workers." Forty years later, in commenting on the importance of these experiments, Dr. Abbot wrote: "[They] have long since been superseded by more accurate observations in modern wind tunnels. Even the conclusions would not now all be considered sound. . . . But a great impetus to aviation was given by the fact that so great a scientist as Langley had devoted himself to a subject which was generally regarded then as the refuge of cranks, nearly in the same class with perpetual motion."

Langley's observations on the soaring of birds led to results which appeared in 1893 in his paper "The Internal Work of the Wind." In this he pointed out that always existing in the wind are "pulsations of sensible magnitude," which he believed were much greater than commonly supposed, and might be a source of power; they might explain the ability of certain birds, such as the turkey buzzard, to soar indefinitely "without any flapping of the wing or any motion other than a slight rocking of the body." "A ship," he said, "is able to go against a head-wind by the force of that wind, owing to the fact that it is partly immersed in the water, which reacts on the keel," and "it is not impossible that a heavy and nearly inert body, *wholly* immersed in the air, can be made to do this." He postulated that the potentiality of "internal work of the wind" was of a very great amount and that an "inclined plane or suitably curved surface, heavier than air, freely immersed in, and moving with the velocity of the mean wind, can . . . be sustained or even raised indefinitely without the expenditure of internal energy." Furthermore, "the mechanical possibility of some advance against the direction of the wind follows."

Langley's task remained to apply his principles "to the art of aerodromics," as he termed it, for he was thoroughly convinced that mechanical flight was not only scientifically possible but practicable. It must not be supposed, however, that this demonstration came about overnight. He was treading new ground, and, being a scientist, he was determined to put the "art of aerodromics" on a scientific basis and if possible release it from the realm of quackery and impracticality with which most people then associated it. He must proceed surely, and every advance must be tested by sound principles of physics.

Langley devoted the next three or four years to the construction of many model flying machines. He tested the experiments of other American and European inventors who had built model planes. He studied engines and fuels. Finally he perfected his so-called Model No. 5, a thirteen-foot steam-powered "aerodrome" weighing only twenty-six pounds. On May 6, 1896, in the presence of Alexander Graham Bell and several other friends, Langley catapulted this model flying machine into the air from a houseboat on the Potomac River. When the engine stopped and the machine had landed safely on the water, it had flown about half a mile.

Six months later he had built a larger model (No. 6), and on November 28, 1896, this machine made a successful flight of three-quarters of a mile in 105 seconds.

These two flights were momentous, in that they very greatly exceeded the work of previous experimenters and proved conclusively the practicability of sustained mechanical flight with a device heavier than air, unmanned but inherently stable. Of these experiments Langley wrote: "I have brought to a close the portion of the work which seemed to be especially mine—the demonstration of the practicability of mechanical flight—and for the next stage, which is the commercial and practical development of the idea, it is probable that the world may look to others. The world, indeed, will be supine if it do not realize that a new possibility has come to it, and that the great universal highway overhead is now soon to be opened."

His prophesy was true, but he himself had not finished his work yet. Naturally, a great deal of public interest had been aroused, and, with the advent of the Spanish-American War, the Government, too, began to take notice. President McKinley became interested, perhaps mindful of the fact that balloons had been successfully used in the Civil War. Early in 1898 a board was appointed, composed of Army and Navy officers, to investigate Langley's experiments and to determine "what the possibilities were of developing a large-size man-carrying machine for war purposes." Their report was favorable, and the Board of Ordnance and Fortification of the War Department allotted $50,000 to Langley for the development, construction, and test of a large aerodrome. The Smithsonian added $20,000 to aid the project.

Work on the machine began, and Langley and his talented engineer, Charles M. Manly, were confronted with one difficult problem after another. But their chief "headache" was to obtain an engine that met their exacting specifications. They made a special trip to Europe to visit builders of automobile engines, but nowhere were they able to find anyone who believed it possible to construct an engine of the necessary power and the required light weight. They returned to America, and Mr. Manly set to work to build the engine himself, in the shops of the Smithsonian Institution. He built a five-cylinder, fifty-two horsepower, water-cooled gasoline engine weighing less than three pounds to the horsepower. It incorporated parts and certain valuable features of design from a rotary engine by Stephen M. Balzer, built under contract and purchased by the Institution.

After many delays, on October 7, 1903—about sixteen years after Langley's first aviation studies at the Allegheny Observatory—the large aerodrome was ready for its first trip. Complete details of the plane's history have been described by Langley and Manly in their "Memoir on Mechanical Flight," published by the Smithsonian five years after Langley's death, and the story of the unsuccessful attempts to fly the plane has been repeated many times. With members of the Board of Ordnance watching, and with Mr. Manly in the aviator's seat, "the machine glided down the launching track," only to plunge into the water under the full power of the engine. It was agreed that the machine had not been properly released into the air and that the front king-post had caught in the launching gear. Little damage was done and Manly was uninjured. The plane was repaired, some slight defects were corrected, and two months later another attempt was made, but with no better success. The machine again plunged into the Potomac. This time, it was said, "the accident was due to the rudder becoming entangled in the launching track, owing to the breakage of some part of the mechanism by which it was connected to the main frame." But whatever the trouble was, it was the virtual end of Langley's aeronautical experiments.

The press and the public were merciless in their criticism and ridicule. They had little of the faith that some of the scientists and inventors had shown and were more convinced than ever that human flight was and always would be impossible. Columnists, cartoonists, and clowns the country over let loose. The Smithsonian and the Government came in for their full share of the jeering.[5] The War Department withdrew its support. "Langley's Folly" was apparently a closed incident.

But the spirit of Icarus must have been abroad that December, for only nine days after Langley's aircraft had "slid into the water like a handful of mortar" (as the *Washington Post* put it) two young Ohio brothers, Wilbur and Orville Wright, flew their heavier-than-air machine over the bleak sand at Kitty Hawk on the Carolina coast. True, the flight was only 120 feet in length and lasted but 10 seconds, but *there was a man aboard*. Somewhat ironically, the event was then little publicized.

Langley's disappointment over the failure of his flying machine to take off must have been keen indeed, for he knew more surely than anybody else just how close he had come to success. There were those who said that the incident broke his heart, but at least one of his best friends said this was not true. "That very night," Cyrus Adler wrote, "I went home with him to his house to dinner. We sat together at his table; we had a good bottle of wine; we smoked some of his excellent cigars. We talked about fairy tales, and other matters which interested us, and the experiment of the day was never alluded to. He seemed in perfectly good humor and quite philosophical." The thing that must have hurt him most, even more than the unjust newspaper and other public criticism, was the antagonism and lack of faith displayed by some of his misunderstanding colleagues. Others, however, endeavored to raise funds to enable him to resume his experiments, and finally the Regents of the Institution appropriated for his use all the income from that part of the Hodgkins Fund that had been given to the Smithsonian in 1891 for re-

[5] See Mark Sullivan's chapter "The Airplane Emerges" (*Our Times*, vol. 2, pp. 553ff, New York, 1927) for a vivid account of the reaction of the public and the press to the invention of the flying machine.

search on atmospheric air in connection with the welfare of man.[6]

This gesture of confidence by the Regents must have raised his spirits, but he had not long to bask in any such aftermath. He was past seventy, and one day in November 1905 he suffered a stroke. From this he partially recovered, and was advised to seek a warmer climate where he could be outdoors. With a favorite niece he went to Aiken, S. C., where early in 1906 he had another attack and died on February 27.

Many years later, during the air raids of World War II, Miss Helen Palmer, editor of the Bureau of American Ethnology, wrote of Langley [7]:

> Pondering the buzzard's flight
>   A genius drew
> The inspiration to translate
>   Man to the blue.
>
> Now deadly fruit of that ascent
>   Holds earth in dread.
> He will not grudge the bitter laurels
>   From his silent head.

Other Aspects of the Secretary

THOUGH LANGLEY POSSESSED an aloofness that contributed greatly to his loneliness, his was a friendly and very human personality. At the office, those who did not know him well believed him to be austere and oversolicitous of the dignity of his position. He was sometimes impatient, irascible, and sharp with his assistants, but those who were closest to him knew that these idiosyncrasies did not rep-

6 This fund, given to the Institution by Thomas G. Hodgkins, of Setauket, N. Y., amounted to nearly $250,000, but the income from only about $142,000 was to be applied to the investigation of atmospheric air. In 1895 a prize of $10,000 derived from this fund was awarded to Lord Rayleigh and Sir William Ramsay of London for discovery of the new element argon.

7 *Scientific Monthly*, November 1946, p. 394.

resent the real man. "He carried for the outer world a shell of hauteur, very unrepresentative of the warm heart within," Dr. Abbot has written.

This basic warmness of his nature was nowhere better illustrated than in his love for children. "I have seen him at the resort Marshall Hall," says Dr. Abbot, "swinging with two little girls, one on either knee, while he told them fairy stories." At the Smithsonian he created the Children's Room, which was one of the chief attractions for young visitors to the Institution until it was dismantled at the beginning of World War II to provide much-needed office space. The room, directly across from the main entrance of the Smithsonian Building, was his special ward, and though he called upon the entire staff to furnish and arrange the exhibits, he appointed himself honorary curator. His acceptance "speech" is worth quoting for its whimsical and genuine nature:

The Secretary of the Smithsonian Institution has been pleased to confer upon me the honorable but arduous duties of the care of the Children's Room. He has at his service so many men learned in natural history that I do not know why he has chosen me, who know so little about it, unless it is because these gentlemen may possibly not be also learned in the ways of children, for whom this little room is meant . . .

Speaking, therefore, in their behalf, and as one of them, I should say that we never have a fair chance in museums. We cannot see the things on the top shelves which only grown-up people are tall enough to look into, and most of the things we can see and would like to know about have Latin words on them which we cannot understand; some things we do not care for at all, and other things, which look entertaining, have nothing on them to tell us what they are about . . .

Some great philosopher has said that "knowledge begins in wonder"; and there is a great deal in the saying. If I may speak of myself, I am sure I remember how the whole studies of my life have been colored by one or two strong impressions received in childhood. The lying down, as a child, in a New England pasture and looking at the mysterious soaring of a hen-hawk far above in the sky, has led me to give many years of mature life to the study of the subject of traveling in air; and puzzling about the way the hotbed I used to see on the farm kept the early vegetables warm under its glass roof has led to many years of study in after life on the way that great hotbed, the earth, is kept warm by its atmosphere; and so on with other things.

Langley was witty and full of fun, too. Dr. Abbot tells that one summer while Langley was in Europe one of the laboratories of the Observatory was built. The door was painted green. On his return he visited the laboratory to see what had been accomplished. As he was leaving he looked at the door and said, "Mr. Abbot, your door reminds me of a little saying we had when I was a boy: 'Neat, not gaudy,' as the Devil said when he painted his tail pea green."

Honors came to Langley from the most outstanding scientific societies and universities in the world, and if he had been a vainglorious man he might have been overwhelmed. In 1895 he was elected a foreign member of the Royal Society of London; he was also a member of the Royal Society of Edinburgh and of the Accademia dei Lincei of Rome and a correspondent of the Institute of France. He was given honorary degrees by both Oxford and Cambridge Universities and by Harvard, Princeton, Michigan, and Wisconsin. He was awarded medals by the Institute of France, the Royal Society, the American Academy of Arts and Sciences, the National Academy of Sciences, and others. Though he belonged to and supported many scientific societies devoted to his interests, he avoided holding office in them, the exceptions being the American Association for the Advancement of Science, of which he was president; the American Philosophical Society, of which he was vice president for a brief time; and the National Academy of Sciences, which he served as vice president and a member of its council. His favorite society seemed to be the Philosophical Society of Washington and before its members he read most of his scientific papers. A flying field near Norfolk, Va., and a laboratory

PLATE 30.   The Langley Medal being presented to Admiral Richard E.
Byrd by Chief Justice Charles Evans Hughes and Secretary Charles G. Abbot

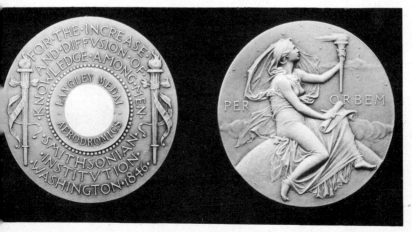

PLATE 31.   Obverse and reverse sides of the Langley Medal

PLATE 32.   Giraffes at the National Zoological Park

PLATE 33.   The bird house, National Zoological Park

of the National Advisory Committee for Aeronautics have been named for him; and in 1947—forty years after his death—another recognition came to him: his name was given to a new unit for use in measuring the sun's heating power. A *langley* is defined as the amount of solar radiation received on one square centimeter capable of raising the temperature of one gram of water one degree Centigrade.

Langley was a profoundly serious man. In whatever field of human thought he entered he sought to keep an open mind, to be a seeker after truth from whatever source it came. In religion, this kept him from being a dogmatist. He was a friend of the Unitarian clergyman Edward Everett Hale and the renowned Swedenborgian the Reverend Frank Sewall. He enjoyed discussing theological questions with Maj. John W. Powell, his outspoken friend and colleague at the Smithsonian. "Mr. Langley and Major Powell," says Dr. Adler, "used to quarrel violently on the subject as to whether there was or was not a soul, or whether there was or was not a future life." He studied the metaphysicians and modern psychologists and even interested himself in psychical research. To quote Dr. Adler again: "He loved to talk with men possessed of positive religious views upon their own beliefs, and had a deep interest in a Jesuit, or a Jew, or a Buddhist, or a Mohammedan, or, indeed, any man who thought he had secured the truth and knew the way of life in this world and the world to come. . . . It seemed to have been one of the necessities of this great mind that it should attempt all the difficult problems which were offered to human observation or curiosity."

His was the true inquiring spirit. "We must not," he wrote in his essay "The Laws of Nature," "consider that anything is absolutely settled or true. . . . The truths of the scientific church are not dogmas, but something put forward as provisional only, and which her most faithful children are welcome to disprove if they can." His faith was, apparently, placed in this kind of progress. Scientific advance could come about only at the expense of old mental guides and old canons of thought. Even the so-called laws of nature he questioned, "for the things that we see from day to day appear permanent only by comparison with the duration of our own brief life, and our own little experience." He might, finally, have said:

> And so, though I may come to grief,
> I put my faith in unbelief.
> And if when I should least expect
> Truth should turn out to be correct,
> Or summer should not follow spring . . .
> I'll be prepared for anything.

Langley was succeeded as Secretary, in 1907, by Charles D. Walcott, a geologist, and the direction of the Smithsonian Institution again passed to a natural scientist. But as we shall see in the following chapters, the spirit of Langley lingered at the Institution for many years. His pioneering work in astrophysics was continued by his assistant Charles G. Abbot, who himself became Secretary in 1928; but his work in aeronautics was culminated when, five years after his death, the Institution published the "Langley Memoir on Mechanical Flight." There was, however, a sequel—the Smithsonian-Wright Brothers controversy—which attracted wide attention. That, however, was not of Langley's time or making and does not belong with his story.

8

A GEOLOGIST TAKES THE HELM

IT HAS BEEN said that the secretaryship of the Smithsonian Institution is the greatest honor that can come
to an American man of science. And the man upon
whom this honor next fell was as deserving of it as was
any of his three predecessors. Like Langley, Charles Doolittle Walcott rose to scientific eminence without benefit
of a college education, but his early talents as a naturalist
were so precocious and so persistently developed that this
did not appear to be a serious handicap. He became one
of the leading paleontologists of his day. As an administrator of scientific organizations and as a public servant
he can well be compared with Spencer Fullerton Baird.
His wide knowledge and interests and experience reached
out into many fields. He was appointed Secretary by the
Board of Regents on January 31, 1907, and served a full
twenty years—until the day of his death, February 9, 1927.
As William Howard Taft, then Chancellor of the Insti-

tution, remarked on the occasion of the Walcott Memorial
Meeting, "Like his predecessors, Henry, Baird, and Langley, his activities in behalf of the Institution were so
comprehensive and constant that he typified, and with
many, he was, the Institution itself."

Early Development

WHEN HE CAME to the Smithsonian Walcott was by no
means a stranger to it or to official life in Washington. In
1883 he had been made honorary curator in the National
Museum and had spent many hours there studying and
identifying fossils. Furthermore, when he became Secretary
he had already been Director of the United States Geological Survey for thirteen years and was well acquainted
with the budgetary and other administrative problems of
a Government agency.

Charles Walcott was the youngest of the four children
of Charles D. and Mary Lane Walcott, of New York Mills,
a small manufacturing town near Utica, N. Y. He was
born on March 31, 1850. At the age of two and a half he
lost his father; and although his grandfather, Benjamin
Walcott, was a well-to-do cotton-mill owner, there was not
complete amity between the two families, and independent Mary Walcott and her four fatherless children were
left pretty much on their own. They moved to Utica and
succeeded in getting along quite respectably without benefit of Grandfather's financial help or sympathy.

Charles was a frail and sickly child, subject to attacks
of asthma, frequent headaches, and backaches. No one
really expected him to live to manhood, but his mother
and particularly his sister nursed and humored him. Jo-
sephine was eight years older than Charles, and she seems
to have taken rather complete charge of her little brother.
The two had much in common, especially a love for nature and the outdoors, and in following this bent the
boy became little by little not only greatly improved in
health but also a promising naturalist. Early he developed

the naturalist's instinct for collecting specimens—birds' eggs, insects, minerals, but chiefly fossils.

He attended the public schools in Utica and the Utica Academy. One of his uncles offered to send him to theological school, but by this time young Walcott had decided that he wanted to follow a career of science and that if he should have a college training it must be directed along the course of his own interests rather than those of others. He got a job in a hardware store but soon left it to work on the farm of William P. Rust, near Trenton Falls. His time was not altogether taken up by agricultural tasks, and, with the help of one of the Rust boys, he continued to collect fossils of the region. Here, also, he met and fell in love with Lura Rust, whom he married on January 9, 1872.

He had interested himself particularly in trilobites, and his first two scientific papers, published in 1875 in the Cincinnati *Quarterly Journal of Science,* described two new species of these fossil crustaceans, which he had discovered near his home at Trenton Falls. He was the first to prove conclusively to the scientific world that trilobites had legs, a feature of much importance in their classification. Later discoveries enabled him to work out the complete anatomy of these animals and their mode of life. These findings were such definite contributions to geologic knowledge that the trilobites soon became important guide fossils throughout the whole Paleozoic era of geologic time.

The trilobites were shelled, segmented, crablike creatures that first appeared on earth about five hundred million years ago in the Cambrian geological period. They were among the first animals to leave any fossil remains. Even at that time these trilobites must have been a very old race, for they were highly developed and specialized. Traces of their presence were first left in the sea-bottom ooze, which gradually was compressed into rock in which their hard shells were preserved. They ranged in size from creatures hardly bigger than ants to some more than eighteen inches long. Apparently they existed in enormous numbers, crawling along the sea bottoms or swimming in the shallow waters of low beaches. For well over one hundred million years they remained the dominant creatures on earth, but some three hundred millions years after their earliest known existence they became extinct. By then the first amphibians were emerging from the seas to become the ancestors of reptiles and mammals. The reason for the trilobites' extinction is completely unknown. Perhaps they were unable to endure a radical change of environment. Or it may be that more efficient animals coming into the seas destroyed them. It was these ancient creatures, an important link in the chain of the earth's geologic history, that challenged young Charles Walcott's scientific interest.

He was already corresponding with other men similarly interested in paleontology, such men as James Hall, New York state geologist; James Dwight Dana, of Yale; E. T. Cox, Indiana geologist, and Louis Agassiz. Authorities recognized his collection of fossils as unique. James Hall declared that it then exceeded in "number, beauty and perfection" all the collections that had been made from the Trenton limestone in New York or in the United States during the preceding fifty years. "No language can convey," he said, "an adequate idea of the beauty and perfection of the trilobites." When Hall learned that the collection was for sale he tried desperately to acquire it for the New York State Museum, but state funds for the purpose were not forthcoming. Walcott finally made a deal with Professor Louis Agassiz at the Museum of Comparative Zoology at Cambridge, and in the autumn of 1872 he accompanied the shipment to its destination.[1]

At Cambridge he met Agassiz and was given the supreme opportunity of studying under the great naturalist. He was even invited to live at the Agassiz home. The plan was for him to make the study of trilobites the major

[1] A second collection, including about 3,500 entire trilobites and owned jointly by Walcott and his brother-in-law William Rust, also went to Cambridge.

of his college course. He returned home inspired, only to learn a few weeks later that Agassiz had died, on December 14, 1873. Thus his chance for a college education disappeared, and he remained at Trenton Falls to nurse his sick wife. But he continued to be his own teacher and to build up his knowledge of geology, particularly that of his own state of New York.

In 1876, after Lura's death, Walcott was invited to become James Hall's assistant at Albany. He was twenty-six years of age, and this was his first big job offer; unhampered by family responsibilities, he accepted. Hall was not an easy man to please, but inasmuch as he was generally regarded as the leading American paleontologist of the time, to work under him was a rare opportunity. Although the two did not always see eye to eye, Walcott convinced Hall of his capabilities. During the three years he stayed at Albany he continued his studies of New York state geology (particularly of the Paleozoic era) and also made trips to Canada, Ohio, and Indiana.

Service with the United States Geological Survey

In 1879 Walcott began his forty-eight-year span of service with the United States Government. The United States Geological Survey had just been organized, with Clarence King as its first director. Upon James Hall's strong recommendation, Walcott was appointed as assistant geologist under King. He took the oath of office on July 21, 1879, and at once started a series of assignments in the West, where the unobscured stratigraphy over a wide region offered vast opportunities to the geologist. He worked in Utah and Nevada. In 1882 he accompanied Maj. John W. Powell, who had just succeeded King as director of the Survey, to the depths of the Grand Canyon of the Colorado, descending from the Kaibab Plateau by a trail built under Powell's direction. Although thirteen years had elapsed since Powell had made his historic navigation of the Colorado, the region was still virtually a *terra incog-*

nita, so much was there yet to be learned of its geography and geology. Walcott's small party stayed in the valley through one winter and returned with "discoveries of the highest interest and value," in Powell's laudatory words.

Walcott's rise was rapid and reads like a success story, except that few financial riches were to be gained as a Government geologist. The reward lay in his increasing scientific prestige, the solid background in paleontology he was acquiring, and the variety of friends he was enabled to make. The summer after he returned to Washington from the Grand Canyon he was honored by election to the Cosmos Club, where he met socially his scientific colleagues and the men with whom later he was to be associated—George Brown Goode, Samuel P. Langley, Cyrus Adler, Alexander Graham Bell, G. K. Gilbert, L. O. Howard, C. Hart Merriam, Harvey W. Wiley, and a host of others. He was evidently well liked by his associates, for a few years later, after he had become director of the Geological Survey, he was elected president of the Club.

His first official connection with the Smithsonian Institution came in 1883, when he was appointed honorary curator in the National Museum's department of invertebrate fossils. This was complementary to his work as Geological Survey paleontologist. He had a room in the southwest corner of the old National Museum Building, now the Arts and Industries Building, where he spent many hours with his fossils, arranging and identifying the Museum's collections in paleontology, and writing reports, which were to appear in the leading geological journals of the country.

Once again he turned to the geology of the New York state region and spent several field seasons in various parts of New York and western Vermont. A heated controversy had arisen among geologists concerning the correctness of the ideas of Dr. Ebenezer Emmons on the geological structure of the Taconic Mountain Range in western Massachusetts and southwestern Vermont. Walcott sought to resolve it by making a detailed study of the rocks of this region. Wrote Powell: "It was largely through Mr. Walcott's labors that the complex relations of the partly classified and greatly disturbed rocks of eastern New York and western New England were made out, and his careful identifications in the field afford a firm foundation for future surveys." In 1888 he went abroad to study the type sections of the Cambrian in Wales, and on his return to Washington was placed in charge of all the Survey's work in invertebrate paleontology.

This position was to lead to another. Major Powell was about to retire as director of the Survey, partly because of ill health and partly under pressure from his critics. During his dozen years of leadership he had done great things for the Survey, but his day was passing, and the prestige of the bureau was so declining that Congress felt impelled to reduce its funds drastically. In January 1894 Powell resigned, to spend his last years directing the work of the Bureau of Ethnology under the Smithsonian, and devoting his time to personal studies in anthropology, psychology, and general philosophy. Walcott was Powell's friend, for he recognized the remarkable worth of this blustering master and tried to help him over his administrative hurdles. Powell, in turn, appreciated Walcott's loyalty and saw him as his logical successor to head the Survey. President Grover Cleveland, whose friendship with Walcott and his sister had begun years before in New York, appointed Walcott director, despite the fact that the two were of different political beliefs.

At the Geological Survey there was much to be done, especially in convincing Congress that the work of the agency deserved and must have increased financial support. At this task Walcott was peculiarly adept. He tried to give the lawmakers facts instead of theories; he knew how to make geology seem important to the country. He talked with a convincing sincerity, with little oratory, but his words were based on a solid background of scientific knowledge. Dr. Abbot recounts:

From long and varied experience he drew wisdom for every emergency. . . . He knew men and how to deal with them. I attended him once at a Congressional sub-committee, when, as he was leaving, a prominent representative said to me that he thought government should not support science except for fully developed utility. As I was arguing the contrary, my chief casually interrupted with what seemed a complete change of subject. The Congressman was interested and Walcott led him on, until, in a moment, my antagonist was facing the proposition that a research which had been begun with no thought of utility five years before, now saved the government millions. As we drove away, I ventured to express my admiration of his adroitness. Dr. Walcott replied, "These lawyers can beat you in argument, but they can't beat plain facts."

When he became director of the Survey in 1894 its appropriation was only $495,990. The first year he succeeded in getting an increase of $72,000; thirteen years later when he left the Survey the appropriation had risen to $1,758,720, and sales of the Survey's publications had increased ninefold. Furthermore, he enlarged the functions of the bureau "to cover investigations of surface and underground waters, the mapping of forest reserves, sectional subdivisions and surveys in the Indian reservations for the Land Office, and the establishment of boundaries of certain Western States." He reorganized the Survey's scientific work, and tried always to keep in mind the taxpayer whom it served. The Western miner and rancher, the Eastern landowner and investor, the student, teacher, and researcher—all must get their dollar's worth. As his successor, George Otis Smith, said, "He united the scientific and the practical, without compromise, in effective service of a type that won acceptance and approval."

Though he was never robust, Walcott could carry on persistent work and adhere to a routine in an indefatigable manner. With all his administrative duties, the social contacts that he had to maintain, and other matters that consumed his time, he kept up his research work at the Museum and nearly every summer went out on a collecting trip. In 1888 he had married Helena Breese Stevens of Rochester. The third of their four children—and only daughter—was born in August after his appointment as Survey director. Walcott was a devoted father and spent much time with his family. Whenever possible they accompanied him on his trips. Mrs. Walcott became quite a proficient assistant.

Wherever there were unexplored fossil-grounds, there Walcott would go, returning with precious brachiopods and trilobites embedded in Cambrian rock. He covered altogether an unbelievable portion of the United States and Canada. Back in Washington the collections had to be organized and studied, new genera and species of fossils described, in this endless effort to piece together the small but significant facts of the earth's history. To quote Smith again: "In those days [he] might commonly be found closeted with his beloved trilobites in the back room, though always ready to turn aside from these messengers from the dim past and equally interested to discuss and decide questions relating to present procedure for the Survey or to the future coal supply for the nation. This devotion to research while under stress of administrative duties was a source of both inspiration and dismay to some of his associates; he did both jobs so well." It was a devotion, too, that lasted throughout his life; the last publication that appears in his bibliography is not an administrative report but a 200-page monograph on the Pre-Devonian Paleozoic formations of the Cordilleran provinces of Canada, published posthumously.

Several Government agencies, which later became full-fledged bureaus, were helped on their way if not actually initiated by Walcott's planning and vision. One of these was the Reclamation Service. Major Powell before him had pioneered in studies of the arid lands of the Western public domain and held concepts far ahead of his time. Together they proposed a plan for irrigating and utilizing portions of these public lands. This would put the areas to valuable agricultural and other purposes, and serve, in addition, to preserve them from speculators and land-grabbers operating under the public-land laws then in effect. The new plan ran counter to these selfish interests, which succeeded in stirring up an attack on Major Powell. "At this critical time," writes Nelson H. Darton, reconnaissance geologist, "Doctor Walcott came to the front and, fearlessly assuming the brunt of these attacks, was able to overcome much of the opposition." He won both the President and the Secretary of the Interior to his views, and the Newlands Reclamation Act became a law on June 17, 1902. This act authorized surveys of irrigable areas and reservoir sites, and preparation of plans for dams and irrigation systems; its result was to save a vast amount of the public domain for the people. While Walcott was director of the Geological Survey the reclamation work was administered by the Survey, under the immediate direction of Dr. F. H. Newell, a prominent engineer and hydrographer. To quote Darton again: "The entire Reclamation program, developed largely under the advisement of Walcott, Newell, and their associates, was a remarkable achievement of persistence and foresight. In its administration he encouraged the initiative of the engineers, overruled petty private consideration, and greatly abbreviated hampering by official red tape and political interference, so that reclamation quickly yielded results of vast utilitarian importance."

Another offshoot of the Geological Survey was the Bureau of Mines, which also began under Walcott's directorship. It had its genesis in 1904 in a Survey project for the analysis and testing of fuels and in an investigation of structural materials begun the next year. From this developed the Survey's Technologic Branch. The work gradually expanded until Congress in 1910 created the Bureau of Mines under the Department of the Interior, with Joseph Austin Holmes, North Carolina geologist, as its first director. The Technologic Branch was the nucleus of the new bureau.

Walcott also had an effective hand in the Government's

pioneer forestry work, which led to the creation of the Forest Service. He had early interested himself in forest conservation, and his extensive travels through the Western states gave him a fine opportunity to know the forests firsthand and recognize their potential worth to the nation. In 1895, largely through his efforts, the first comprehensive law organizing the forest reserves of the country was passed, and an appropriation was given the Geological Survey "to separate and survey a vast area of forested lands suitable for forest reservations." His role in this pioneering forestry-conservation work is described by Darton: "He drafted most of the provisions of the various laws, and by personal influence with leading Congressmen was able to avert much of the strong lobby of opposition which was marshaled by persons selfishly interested in lumber and other features in the western forested areas. The product of this work was the Forest Service, which under the administration of Gifford Pinchot and his successors has saved the remnants of our great forests which were formerly devastated by selfish private interests."

Establishment of the Carnegie Institution

WALCOTT'S VARIOUS SUCCESSES encouraged him to attempt others. Of no small significance in their accomplishment was his facility in winning the confidence of influential people. They respected him as a scientist and as a friend, and trusted his judgment and sought his advice. It will be recalled that this was a period in which the ability to command the attention of captains of industry was beginning to bring material rewards. Early in the century Andrew Carnegie, believing that "the man who dies rich dies disgraced," made the first of his lavish philanthropies —$10,000,000 in United States Steel Corporation bonds to Scotch universities and $1,500,000 to build the temple of peace for the Hague Court of Arbitration. Other holders of great wealth were making generous contributions to worthy projects. John D. Rockefeller gave $7,000,000 for search for a tuberculosis serum; Cecil Rhodes bequeathed $10,000,000 to provide scholarships for American youths at Oxford University; Joseph Pulitzer donated $2,000,000 to found a school of journalism at Columbia University. A Chicago poet satirized the situation:

> Let us then be up and doing,
>   All becoming money kings;
> Some day we may be endowing
>   Universities and things.
> Lives of billionaires remind us
>   That we've got to own the stock
> If we want to leave behind us
>   Libraries on every block.[2]

Scientists everywhere were seeking funds for research, and in Washington a group wondered how they, too, might benefit. The time seemed propitious for trying to obtain substantial assistance. A plan was formulated for the establishment of a national scientific research institution in Washington, honoring the first President, and to Walcott, as mediator of the group, was delegated the responsibility of outlining it to two of the wealthiest men in the country. Walcott's skillful presentation of the plans of the scientists evoked a favorable response from Andrew Carnegie. Much deliberation and discussion with leading scientists followed. Finally, on November 28, 1901, Carnegie wrote to President Theodore Roosevelt: "Mr. President, believe me that I am made a very happy man this day of Thanksgiving by the thought that I have been so favored as to be enabled to prove, at least in some degree, my gratitude to and love for the Republic to which I owe so much." Within a few days it was announced that he would give $10,000,000 to establish a research institution in the Nation's Capital. The gift was consummated on January 28, 1902; the establishment was to be known as the Carnegie Institution of Washington with the purpose of encouraging "in the broadest and most liberal

2 Quoted in *Our Times*, vol. 1, by Mark Sullivan.

manner investigation, research, and discovery, and the application of knowledge to the improvement of Mankind."

Walcott worked behind the scenes with Daniel C. Gilman, John S. Billings, Nicholas Murray Butler, and other institutional leaders. He was secretary of the board of incorporators and helped draw up the articles of incorporation for the new establishment; later he served on its board of trustees and executive committee. All this was invaluable experience. Creation of the Carnegie Institution was truly a victory for science, but for Walcott it was another step toward the position he was finally to reach.

The Smithsonian's Fourth Secretary

THAT POSITION was the secretaryship of the Smithsonian. It is doubtful whether in 1902 he even hoped to attain that honor, but five years later, following the death of Secretary Langley, he seemed to many the most logical man for the job. First choice of the Regents was Henry Fairfield Osborn, the renowned vertebrate paleontologist of the American Museum of Natural History. But Osborn declined the honor, and on January 23, 1907, Walcott was elected Secretary. President Theodore Roosevelt wrote him: "The only consolation about your leaving [the Geological Survey] is that in the Smithsonian Institution you will again do a work which, so far as I know, no other man in this country could do quite as well." Walcott had every intention of carrying on his research; to his laboratory in the Smithsonian went 900 drawers of Cambrian fossils from the Geological Survey.

During his colorful administration which ended on March 4, 1909, Theodore Roosevelt had made significant contributions to domestic advancement. With his $40,000 Nobel peace-prize money, awarded for his aid in terminating the Russo-Japanese War, he established a Foundation for the Promotion of Industrial Peace. With Harvey W. Wiley he had brought about pure-food legislation. With Gifford Pinchot and others he had aroused the country to the need for the conservation of natural resources. He had won a final political victory by virtually appointing his Presidential successor, William Howard Taft. And now, a little past fifty and still the vigorous "T. R.," he was on his way out, but he did not intend to shun the limelight. While in the Geological Survey, Walcott had been one of Roosevelt's close advisers and friends, and in June 1908 the President made him a proposition. From Oyster Bay he wrote:

About the 1st of April next I intend to start for Africa. . . . By May 1 I shall land at Mombasa and spend the next few months hunting and traveling in British and German East Africa; probably going thence to or toward Uganda. . . . As you know, I am not in the least a game butcher. I like to do a certain amount of hunting, but my real and main interest is the interest of a faunal naturalist. Now, it seems to me that this opens the best chance for the National Museum to get a fine collection not only of the big game beasts, but of the smaller mammals and birds of Africa. . .

Roosevelt proposed to do the hunting and agreed to turn over his specimens to the National Museum if the Smithsonian would furnish field naturalists to accompany him and transport the trophies to America. Walcott immediately accepted the offer; a special fund was raised from "friends of the Smithsonian Institution" to meet the expenses of the naturalists; and the expedition sailed from New York on March 23, 1909. Colonel Roosevelt was accompanied by his son Kermit and three naturalists—Lt. Col. Edgar A. Mearns, Edmund Heller, and J. Alden Loring. They arrived in Africa on April 21.

The results were spectacular. Large collections of birds, small mammals, and big game came to the Museum, and even today the Roosevelt African collection of animals in the Natural History Building is one of the most popular exhibits, though naturally forty years have seen great improvements in display techniques. It was a proud moment for the Museum when the collection was finally installed. It was as much a testimony to Secretary Walcott's vision

PLATE 34. Astrophysical Observatory Station at Mount Montezuma, Chile

PLATE 35. View of the Smithsonian Building used on the Smithsonian Centennial 3-cent postage stamp issued in 1946 (*Photo by Floyd B. Kestner, 1946*)

PLATE 36. Alexander Wetmore, elected secretary of the
Smithsonian Institution in 1945

PLATE 37. Arts and Industries and Smithsonian Buildings from the east
(Photo by John O. Brostrup, 1947)

and alertness as an administrator as it was to the abilities of the great Nimrod "Teddy" Roosevelt.

Another of Secretary Walcott's accomplishments was his seeing through to completion the construction of the New National Museum Building, now usually referred to as the Natural History Building. It was the third great building to be erected in the Smithsonian group and had been long awaited. The old National Museum, built to house the influx of material from the Philadelphia Centennial of 1876, had long been bulging as the national collections in science, industry, and history continued to accumulate. The new building promised to give the museum elbow room again and provide a safer depository for some of the real treasures of the American people.

Congress finally appropriated funds for the erection of the new building; on June 15, 1904, Secretary Langley broke ground at the foot of Tenth Street, N.W., on what is now Constitution Avenue. By the time the excavation and foundations were completed Langley had died, however, and when the cornerstone was laid, on October 15, 1906, Dr. Walcott had taken over.

Monumental in scale, suited to the position it occupied in the Capital's Mall, the building incorporated the latest developments in museum construction. Its design was classic, finished on all sides in granite. The floor area of the four stories totaled more than 10 acres; the frontage measured 561 feet, the depth 365 feet, and the height 82 feet. An octagonal rotunda, 80 feet in diameter, with four massive stone piers and a curved tiled ceiling, reached a height of 124½ feet. The building cost three and a half million dollars and was completed on June 20, 1911, although portions of it had been opened to the public in March of the previous year. Upon Assistant Secretary Richard Rathbun fell much of the burden of seeing the new building through to completion. It was a great day for the Smithsonian when the museum curators moved into their new offices and the cluttered collections and cramped exhibits could be reinstated in the commodious marble halls. For the first time there was room enough for both exhibition and study materials. Unfortunately, however, the situation was too good to last many years, and today, as this is written, the Natural History Building, housing three large museum departments (zoology, geology, and anthropology), the National Collection of Fine Arts, and a large scientific library, is full to overflowing, as the Smithsonian waits again for Congress to provide it more and ampler buildings.

Field Work in the West

IN SPITE OF the heavy responsibilities of administering the affairs of the Smithsonian, Walcott managed every summer to continue his geological field work. Year after year he returned to the Canadian Rockies to study the Cambrian and other rocks and gather fossils. He sent tons of them back to Washington for study during the winter. His reports on these collections brought him further world-wide recognition by geologists. One of his finest pieces of work was carried on in British Columbia, where he found a priceless deposit of Cambrian fossils near Burgess Pass. He quarried this Burgess shale systematically, took magnificent panoramic photographs, and made many geologic discoveries.

For some summers after 1907 Walcott was engaged in field studies on the geologic structure and in collecting fossils in the extraordinary thickness of over twelve thousand feet of Cambrian deposits in the Rocky Mountains. In the field season of 1909, while descending Mount Wapta in British Columbia, Mrs. Walcott's horse slipped and upturned a slab that exposed the first specimen of a fauna of 70 genera and 130 species of Middle Cambrian fossils. Their internal structure was most remarkably preserved; several volumes were required to include a complete description and the full results of some years of research which Walcott devoted to them.

The scientific importance of Walcott's work is well stated by Dr. T. C. Chamberlin in the *Journal of Geology:*

Charles Doolittle Walcott did many things and did them well but his persistent effort to elucidate the earth's earliest record of life will be his lasting monument. His choice of this field was strategic. No faunas of the past mean so much to those who want to know the salient things about the history of life on the planet. Our base line for projecting estimates into the great unrecorded era of primitive life has its distal end on the Cambrian fauna and its proximate end on the life of today. Walcott worked with a success equaled by no other in giving a definite placement to the farther end of this base line. The revelations of its nature that rewarded his search in his later years were quite beyond the fondest expectations. He found evidence that, as long ago as the Cambrian, life bore many features closely like those of the life of today. These revelations have made clear that the life of that day was very far from being "primordial." The base line must be multiplied many times before the true primordial life can be reached.

The great significance of Walcott's work lies in this determination. The wonderful record of details of life structure he was so fortunate as to recover—perhaps we should say he had the acumen to uncover—makes his contribution secure and explicit. His monument rests on a solid foundation. Its value as a standard of measurement will be better realized as time goes on and the real age of the earth and the slowness of life evolution comes to be more fully appreciated.

Aeronautical Activities

ANOTHER MAJOR INTEREST in Walcott's career drew him into national prominence—as well as into a strange controversy. This interest was aeronautics. Unlike his predecessor, Secretary Langley, he was not a technical airman. But he was a guiding spirit who had confidence in the future of aviation. First of all he had believed in his friend Langley, and knew all about his repeated successful flights with steam-driven model aerodromes in 1896; it was Walcott who in 1898 first called them to President McKinley's attention and suggested to him that flying machines might be used in the Spanish-American War.

We must admire Walcott for his devotion to Langley and his faith in his work. In 1914, about ten years after the failure of the Langley plane, a last attempt was made to determine whether this plane had been capable of sustained free flight. It was suggested to Walcott that the Langley plane be reconstructed according to original specifications and given another chance to vindicate its inventor. To describe what happened, let us quote the latest official Smithsonian account (1942), by Dr. C. G. Abbot:

In March 1914, Secretary Walcott contracted with Glenn H. Curtiss to attempt a flight with the Langley machine. This action seems ill considered and open to criticism. For in January 1914, the United States Court of Appeals, Second Circuit, had handed down a decision recognizing the Wrights as "pioneers in the practical art of flying with heavier-than-air machines" and pronouncing Glenn H. Curtiss an infringer of their patent. Hence, in view of probable further litigation, the Wrights stood to lose in fame and revenue and Curtiss stood to gain pecuniarily, should the experiments at Hammondsport indicate that Langley's plane was capable of sustained flight in 1903, previous to the successful flights made December 17, 1903, by the Wrights at Kitty Hawk, N. C.

The machine was shipped to Hammondsport, N. Y., in April. Dr. Zahm, the Recorder of the Langley Aerodynamical Laboratory and expert witness for Curtiss in the patent litigation, was at Hammondsport as official representative of the Smithsonian Institution during the time the machine was being reconstructed and tested. In the reconstruction the machine was changed from what it was in 1903 in a number of particulars. . . . On the 28th of May and the 2d of June, 1914, attempts to fly were made. After acquiring speed by running on hydroplane floats on the surface of Lake Keuka the machine lifted into the air several different times. The longest time off the water with the Langley motor was approximately five seconds. Dr. Zahm stated that "it was apparent that owing to the great weight which had been given to the structure by adding the floats it was necessary to increase the propeller thrust." So no further attempts were made to fly with the Langley 52 HP engine.

The Smithsonian, however, published statements to the effect that the 1914 experiment had shown that Langley's plane of 1903 without essential modification was the first heavier-than-air machine capable of maintaining sustained human flight. When the restored Langley plane was first placed on exhibit in the National Museum on January 15, 1918, it bore this label: "The Original, Full-size Langley Flying Machine, 1903." Later another label was substituted containing the claim that Langley's machine was "the first man-carrying aeroplane in the history of the world capable of sustained free flight," and still later this statement was modified by including the words "in the opinion of many competent to judge." These statements met with the disapproval and resentment of Orville Wright [3] and caused him in 1928 to send his original Kitty Hawk machine "in exile" to the Science Museum at South Kensington, England, instead of to the Smithsonian Institution. As long as Walcott was Secretary, this unfortunate Smithsonian-Wright controversy remained uncomposed and flared up perennially. Secretary Abbot, convinced that the Institution had been in the wrong and that his predecessor had acted unwisely in the matter, published an official statement of correction and apology, concluding: "If the publication of this paper should clear the way for Dr. Wright to bring back to America the Kitty Hawk machine to which all the world awards first place, it will be a source of profound and enduring gratification to his countrymen everywhere. Should he decide to deposit the plane in the United States National Museum, it would be given the highest place of honor, which is its due." [4] Orville Wright expressed his satisfaction, but when he died on January 30, 1948, his plane was still in England.

[3] Wilbur Wright had died in 1912.
[4] Abbot, C. G., "The 1914 Tests of the Langley 'Aerodrome,'" *Smithsonian Misc. Coll.*, vol. 103, No. 8 (Oct. 24, 1942).

After Wright's death the executors of his estate agreed that it had been his intention that the plane should ultimately be returned to the United States, and finally arrangements were concluded for its deposit in the United States National Museum. The Institution expected its arrival before the end of 1948.

No one will deny that during his secretaryship Walcott advanced the science of aeronautics. On his recommendation the Board of Regents in 1908 established the Langley Medal, to be awarded by the Smithsonian "for specially meritorious investigations in connection with the science of aerodromics and its application to aviation." In the forty years since, the medal has been awarded seven times:

> Wilbur and Orville Wright, 1909
> Glenn H. Curtiss, 1913
> Gustave Eiffel, 1913
> Charles A. Lindbergh, 1927
> Richard E. Byrd, 1929
> Charles M. Manly (posthumously), 1929
> Joseph S. Ames, 1935

Walcott was greatly interested in building up the National Museum aircraft collections portraying the history and development of aeronautics. Finding adequate space in the Smithsonian buildings for this collection has always been a problem, for none of them were designed to hold dozens of full-size airplanes. The influx of material during the years of World War I was partially provided for by the procurement of the Aircraft Building, a hangarlike steel structure originally used as a testing laboratory for the Liberty engine. It was opened to the public in 1920. But even with this added room, the Museum has had to refuse much valuable historical material. More than a dozen planes, including Langley's 1896 models, the Langley Aerodrome, the Wright Brothers' military plane of 1909, Lindbergh's *Spirit of St. Louis,* and Wiley Post's *Winnie Mae,* are suspended from the ceiling of the Arts and Industries Building. In 1946 Congress created the

National Air Museum as a bureau of the Smithsonian, and the national aircraft collection became the nucleus of the new agency. As this is written, this museum is in process of organization.

Important, too, was the part Walcott played in the formation of the National Advisory Committee for Aeronautics,[5] which today ranks as one of the top-flight national councils. Walcott's vision brought the Committee into being. When World War I began in Europe, thoughts in this country turned to preparedness. It became apparent that aviation, the new weapon, was to play a role in the war, and Dr. Walcott was one of those who foresaw that the development of aeronautics for military purposes must have a sound scientific foundation. He worked for the passage of the NACA enabling act, which President Wilson signed on March 3, 1915, and by the time the United States entered the war in 1917 the work of the Committee was well under way, with Walcott serving as chairman of its executive committee. Under his direction it set up a research laboratory at what is now Langley Field, near Hampton, Va., named in honor of Dr. Langley. Much research has been performed at this and the NACA's other two laboratories, as evidenced in hundreds of technical reports, invaluable to engineers, designers, and manufacturers, and to the national defense.

Another achievement of the Committee was its assistance in settling the patent dispute that threatened to im-

[5] On May 1, 1913, the Smithsonian Regents approved a general scheme submitted by Secretary Walcott "to reopen the Langley Aerodynamical Laboratory; to appoint an Advisory Committee; to add, as means are provided, other laboratories and agencies; to group them into a bureau organization; and to secure the cooperation with them of the Government and other agencies." The purpose of the laboratory was to be the study of the problems of aerodynamics, with such research and experimentation as might be necessary to increase the safety and effectiveness of aerial locomotion for the purposes of commerce, national defense, and the welfare of man. The Advisory Committee was appointed, but soon thereafter for legal reasons it was found necessary to discontinue it. It was, however, together with the plans for the Laboratory, the real forerunner of the National Advisory Committee for Aeronautics.

pede the Government's aviation efforts in the war and even retarded its acquisition of planes. As N. H. Darton has described it, "Dr. Walcott and his subcommittee on patents evolved a 'cross-license agreement' which brought an end to the patent controversy and made possible the financing of expansion projects." The agreement was upheld by the courts and by the Comptroller General. It was indicative of the kind of liaison work between industry and Government that had to be done in wartime aviation and that the Committee has continued to the present time. The complete story of the Committee's achievements is too long for detailing here. Walcott's interest in it during its first dozen years was its very lifeblood. Said Joseph S. Ames, chairman of the NACA from 1927 to 1939, "He created it; he planned its duties wisely; he guided and inspired it; he secured the appropriation for its support. Each year he took more interest and pride in its operation. There can be no doubt but that from all this he himself received his reward of pleasure and satisfaction."

Other Interests and Accomplishments

IN THE NACA Walcott's ability as an organizer was most strikingly shown, even though it had already been aptly demonstrated in his work with the Geological Survey, the Carnegie Institution, and other agencies. He was active in the work of many scientific organizations, including the National Academy of Sciences, and his election to the presidency of the Academy he considered one of the highest honors he ever received. He was constantly serving on committees of one kind or another and seemed to be in his natural element when doing work that brought him in contact with many and diverse people. Furthermore, it was a relief from and contrast to the close and meticulous application that his paleontology required. Indeed, he led three lives, each with distinction: the life of the exact laboratory scientist, the life of the exploring field-geologist, and the life of the administrator and organizer.

As we have seen, Walcott had a persuasive knack for getting money not only from Congress but also from private philanthropists in aid of science. The Smithsonian, never a rich institution, and continuously hampered by lack of funds for all it wished to accomplish, needed such a man as Secretary; it has been the consensus that had the war not intervened to consume so much of his energies, he would have done greater things financially for the Institution. Even so, several large bequests were made to the Smithsonian during the twenty years he was Secretary:

In 1911, an estate estimated at $40,000 came from Lucy T. and George W. Poore, for the general use of the Institution when the principal shall amount to $250,000.

In 1912, Dr. Frederick G. Cottrell, chemist of the United States Bureau of Mines, offered the Smithsonian his patents "relating to the electrical precipitation of dust, smoke, and chemical fumes."

[At Cottrell's and Walcott's instigation, a separate organization—the Research Corporation of New York—was established to administer for the benefit of research the funds thus accruing. The objects of the Corporation are: "First, to acquire inventions and patents and to make them more available in the arts and industries, while using them as a source of income, and, second, to apply all profits derived from such use to the advancement of technical and scientific investigation and experimentation through the agency of the Smithsonian Institution and such other scientific and educational institutions and societies as may be selected by the directors." In the years since 1912 the income of the Corporation has been built up and large grants have been made for research. The Smithsonian has received considerable sums during later years through the Corporation, especially for the work of the Division of Radiation and Organisms before the support of this agency was assumed by the Federal Government. The Secretary of the Smithsonian is a member of the Corporation's board of directors.]

In 1913, Dr. Leander T. Chamberlain bequeathed

$25,000 to be known as the Frances Lea Chamberlain fund, for "promoting the increase, and the scientific value and usefulness, of the Isaac Lea collection of gems and gem material" and $10,000 to be used for "promoting the scientific value and usefulness of the Isaac Lea collection of mollusks."

In 1916, Charles L. Freer donated $1,000,000 for the immediate erection of the Freer Gallery of Art Building.

In 1919, Mrs. Virginia Purdy Bacon bequeathed $50,000 to establish the Walter Rathbone Bacon Traveling Scholarship for the study of the faunas of countries other than the United States.

In 1920, the Institution inherited $25,000 from Morris Loeb for the Loeb collection of chemical types.

In 1920, John A. Roebling started a series of contributions (amounting to more than half a million dollars) for the work of the Astrophysical Observatory.

In 1922, Dr. Walcott himself, with Mrs. Walcott, established a research fund amounting to $11,520.

In 1925, the National Geographic Society made a grant of $55,000 to select a site and to equip a solar-radiation station in the Eastern Hemisphere.

In 1926, Frederick A. Canfield bequeathed his large collection of precious mineral specimens, with an endowment of $50,000 for its care and development.

Finally, in the last years of his administration, Walcott projected a campaign to raise $10,000,000 for the Smithsonian's general endowment fund. The drive started off auspiciously but was interrupted by Dr. Walcott's death and was never actually consummated.

The years of World War I were hard ones for the Smithsonian, as they were for all institutions. Military matters had to take precedence over "business-as-usual" and the routine "increase and diffusion of knowledge." The resources of its staff and laboratories were turned toward helping win the war, in whatever ways they could. Much important information was furnished to the war agencies, and special lines of research were undertaken. In the

Astrophysical Observatory, for example, some of the problems investigated were the pressure of wind on projectiles, the designing of a recoilless gun for the Signal Corps, and the study of suitable searchlights for Army use. The Bureau of War Risk Insurance of the Treasury Department was given office space in the Natural History Building; at one time accommodations were provided for more than 3,000 employees, and the building was closed to the public.

The burden on Dr. Walcott was heavy, and tragedy, striking his home three times in the span of half a dozen years, increased this burden. First, in 1911, his wife Helena Stevens Walcott had been instantly killed in a railroad accident; then in the spring of 1913 his eldest son, Charles, died of tuberculosis. The third blow came on December 12, 1917, when another son, Benjamin Stuart Walcott, of the Lafayette Escadrille, was killed while on patrol duty behind the German lines.

At the age of sixty-four, on June 30, 1914, Walcott married again, this time to Mary Morris Vaux, of a well-to-do Philadelphia Quaker family. The marriage proved to be a most felicitous one. Ten years his junior, Mary was an energetic mountain climber, a fine photographer, a student of glacial geology, a talented artist, and a woman fully sympathetic to Walcott's scientific interests. They traveled and studied the West together, climbed mountains, hunted fossils, took pictures—an unusual couple. The beautiful quarto portfolios, *Wild Flowers of North America,* published by the Smithsonian beginning in 1926, are a testimonial to Mary Vaux's artistic abilities, but her greatest contribution was the happiness and companionship she brought to Charles Walcott during the last dozen years of his life. When Mrs. Walcott died in 1940, she bequeathed $400,000 to the Institution to be added to the fund that Dr. Walcott and she had established for geological research and publication.

To the very end Dr. Walcott was looking forward and planning great things for the Smithsonian. In fact, an important conference to discuss the future of the Institution was held on February 11, 1927, at which the President, the Vice President, members of the Cabinet, and a group of the foremost American scientists and industrial leaders met under the chairmanship of Chief Justice William Howard Taft. This conference was planned and organized by Secretary Walcott, and he was to have taken a leading part in it, but a short time before it was held he suffered an apoplectic stroke and died two days before the meeting. Wisely, the conference was not postponed, and it served as a timely guide to the man who was to follow in Walcott's footsteps—Dr. Charles Greeley Abbot —although its main objective, to bring about a very substantial increase of the Smithsonian's endowment, never fully materialized.[6]

Charles D. Walcott was a great scientist and a great man. He was also a man of faith. As the editor of the *Outlook* wrote, "He was a man of spiritual insight, and though he knew as a scientist how to weigh and measure he valued most highly those things that are measureless and imponderable."

6 One of the principal addresses of the conference was made by Regent Dwight W. Morrow, who had an active part in organizing it and who later gave $150,000 to the Institution's endowment fund.

9

ROUNDING OUT A CENTURY

THE NAME of Charles Greeley Abbot has appeared frequently in these pages, and some of his accomplishments have already been detailed in the chapters on Langley and Walcott. As fifth Secretary of the Smithsonian, Dr. Abbot steered the course of the Institution through the dark days of the depression and the early years of World War II, and when he resigned from his office in 1944 he left a record of scientific achievement for himself and definite growth for the Institution. Unlike his predecessor, Dr. Abbot was never fond of administrative work, but was happiest when carrying on his researches, at the Astrophysical Observatory in Washington, at Mount Wilson Observatory in California, and at other places throughout the world where solar investigations might be in progress. After serving seventeen years, he retired from the secretaryship in order to devote his remaining years to scientific research.

He was born on a farm at Wilton, N. H., on May 31, 1872. His grandmother, Rebekah Hale, was a niece of Nathan Hale, the American patriot. Young Abbot early developed a technical facility and inventiveness that later were to serve him well. He tells us that before he was big enough to work on the farm he soldered copper pans and mended enamel ones for the household, using the kitchen stove as a torch. At thirteen he built for himself a forge with which he mended farm implements. He constructed a high-wheeled wooden bicycle with iron tires, rigged up a wooden waterwheel on a small stream, and from a tin can fashioned a saw capable of cutting up half-rotten wood.

After graduating from the village high school and attending Phillips Academy at Andover, Mass., for a year, he passed the entrance examinations for the Massachusetts Institute of Technology, with the intention of studying chemical engineering. When part way through his course, on the advice of one of his professors, Dr. A. A. Noyes, he converted to physics, and in spite of the extra work that this entailed he graduated in 1894 with high honors. After graduation he was offered a place as an assistant in the physical laboratory at M.I.T., which enabled him to take his master of science degree while working. At the end of one year opportunity came to him when Secretary Langley asked Professor Cross of M.I.T. to recommend an assistant for the Astrophysical Observatory. Abbot was selected, and in the hot summer of 1895 he journeyed to Washington to start his new job.

First Years with the Smithsonian

ABBOT'S FIRST notable research work had been in collaboration with Dr. Noyes, a study of the dissociation values of certain chemicals, in which Abbot made hundreds of chemical analyses of great delicacy and accuracy. In Washington his investigations were of a different nature. Langley had already invented the bolometer and with its aid was trying to plot the Fraunhofer lines in the invisible infrared spectrum. Abbot improved the delicacy of this instrument, so that the effect of the earth's jarring and trembling, as well as temperature effects, was largely eliminated. He also improved the galvanometer used by Langley.

In 1902 Langley, with Abbot as his assistant, renewed [1] his studies of solar-radiation intensity to determine the total degree of variability of the sun's radiation, its absorption by the atmospheres both of the sun and of the earth, and the effects upon climate. In this work Abbot developed another new instrument—the silver-disk pyrheliometer—which measures in calories per square centimeter per minute the intensity of the sun's rays received at the earth's surface. Pyrheliometers are now widely used at observatories throughout the world; in fact, about a hundred of them have been built at the Smithsonian and distributed at cost.

Langley's solar studies have already been discussed in a former chapter. In those of later years Abbot was a collaborator, and at Langley's death in 1906 Abbot was the man to carry them on. On March 1, 1907, he was appointed director of the Astrophysical Observatory, and for thirty-seven years he was actively in charge of the work, even during the years he was Secretary. He expanded the operations of the Observatory along many lines. With his improved instruments he refined and corrected Langley's measurement of the solar constant. In 1907 and 1910, while colleagues observed on Mount Wilson, Calif., Dr. Abbot made complete solar-constant observations at the summit of Mount Whitney at 14,500 feet and demonstrated that the methods of measurement used gave results independent of the altitude of the observer.

Another test undertaken was to find the nature of variations in the sun's heat. Were the variations really solar, or were they caused by obscure atmospheric sources of

[1] As long before as 1881 Langley had measured the solar constant while on the Mount Whitney Expedition.

error not yet eliminated? Dr. Abbot went to Algeria to make observations, to be compared with those at Mount Wilson. It was concluded that the variations are not caused by local atmospheric conditions, but are actually solar. Many other experiments and tests were made under Abbot's direction to corroborate the Smithsonian's measurements of the solar constant and eliminate all possible errors.

As we have seen, the Smithsonian pioneered in weather recording; its early meteorological studies under Joseph Henry led to the establishment of the Weather Bureau and the modern system of weather forecasting. Now Dr. Abbot's solar studies were to be definitely applied to meteorology. The probable relationship between solar variation and the weather was first suggested in 1917 by H. H. Clayton, who was then chief forecaster for the Argentine Government Weather Bureau and who had been studying some of the Smithsonian data. Dr. Abbot was convinced that this relationship existed and spent three decades in work designed to prove it scientifically, although some of his theories were not accepted by other meteorologists. It was necessary to obtain accurate values for the solar constant for as many days as possible over a wide geographic range. The Astrophysical Observatory established a number of high-altitude stations where instruments were installed and observations made by trained observers. The first of these was located near Calama, Chile (later moved to Mount Montezuma, Chile); the second was at Mount Harqua Hala, Ariz. (later moved to Table Mountain, Calif.); and the third at Mount Brukkaros, South West Africa (after five years moved to Mount St. Katherine near Mount Sinai, Egypt). Another was established at Burro Mountain, N. Mex. Other locations have since been used. Funds for the work were furnished in large part by John A. Roebling of New Jersey; the observatory on Mount St. Katherine was financed through a grant from the National Geographic Society; and the income of certain of the Smithsonian endowments con-

PLATE 38. Front view of the National Gallery of Art
(Photo by Courtesy of the Gallery)

PLATE 39. Part of the "Main Hall" exhibit in the Smithsonian Building, showing a cross section of the Institution's activities

tributed substantially. Over a period of years a large volume of measurements was collected, until finally Mr. Clayton and Dr. Abbot were able to publish some significant deductions.

For about two years Mr. Roebling supported a research bureau under Clayton's direction to test the relations which might exist between the sun's variation and the weather of the United States. Before long, definite predictions were possible. Telegrams giving the state of the sun of the day before were sent daily to Clayton, and he replied on the same afternoon with predictions of the temperature for New York City. After two years of trial, mathematical analysis indicated prevision up to five days. Many interesting results from these studies were published by the Smithsonian.

As the years passed and the solar data accumulated, more and more results were forthcoming from Abbot's researches. He worked out definite periodicities of solar variation that partially matched terrestrial temperature curves. All were designed toward his aim of applying his work directly to long-range weather forecasting, when the great mass of solar statistics gathered at the Smithsonian stations should yield their results. In 1947 Dr. Abbot announced the discovery of a "cosmic week"—a period of 6.6456 days, which appears both in variations of the radiation output of the sun and variations in temperature at three selected Weather Bureau stations, based on records of thirty-five years and subjected to mathematical analysis. The cycle is remarkable, he found, because of its regularity, pointing still more strongly to a close relation between solar radiation and weather on the earth.

In 1923 and 1924 he devised an instrument to measure the heat of stellar spectra, so sensitive as to be able to measure the heat of a match 2,000 miles away if no atmosphere intervened. He measured the heat of ten of the brighter stars, and afterward constructed a radiometer, using fly wings, ten times more sensitive than his previous instrument.

In 1929 Dr. Abbot established in the Smithsonian a Division of Radiation and Organisms—a direct outgrowth of Langley and Abbot's studies of the solar spectrum. This agency inaugurated a new type of research to discover the effects of radiation of various types and of various wave lengths upon living organisms, mainly plants. At first the work was supported chiefly by funds granted by the Research Corporation of New York, but about 1941 it was taken over under Governmental appropriations as one of the continuing functions of the Smithsonian. One typical piece of research that the Division performed was the determination of the relative efficiencies of different wave lengths to promote photosynthesis in wheat. It was found that rays of wave lengths less than 4,000 Ångstroms or more than 7,500 Ångstroms were totally ineffective in photosynthesis. W. P. True has written: "Like other phases of Smithsonian research, this work is fundamental in character and is not restricted to work of an immediately practical nature. The effort is to discover basic laws and principles, in the sure knowledge that all such discoveries will eventually be put to use in promoting the welfare of mankind."

Since Galileo, it seems, astronomers have been celebrated for their ability to devise new scientific instruments. Dr. Abbot is no exception. In one of the wooden buildings south of the Smithsonian Building is a machine shop ancient of days but still alive with activity. Here among the lathes and pulleys works Andrew Kramer, instrument maker, who helped Samuel P. Langley and Charles Manly build their strange aeronautical "contraptions," who has built dozens of pyrheliometers, and has constructed most of the fine apparatus that has emanated from the Astrophysical Observatory. And here now, almost any day of the week, white-haired Charles G. Abbot may be seen, "retired" but busier than ever, working over some new instrument with Andrew Kramer. Here he built his solar-heat collectors, which utilized the sun's primal energy to run a small motor or to bake bread—

devices that today may seem mere playthings but that someday, when other sources of power have diminished (as they threaten to do), may be regarded as highly as was Henry's electromagnet or Langley's aerodrome. As Abbot himself has said, in another connection, "Who knows when he goes about an investigation to increase the bounds of knowledge, however remote his subject may be from the ordinary walks of life, what application the future may have in store for the results he gains?"

Dr. Abbot's solar heater, which was widely publicized just before World War II, was developed upon simple but ingenious principles. The sun rays, meeting a parabolic cylindric concave mirror surface, are reflected to a line focus in a glass tube, where they are absorbed to produce heat in a certain black liquid with a high boiling point. The heated liquid rises to a reservoir above, and a return tube under the mirror completes the circulation.

Two applications of this heater were made and described by Dr. Abbot. The first was a device used on Mount Wilson, Calif., for cooking. The reservoir above the mirror contained two ovens. The temperature reached was high enough to bake bread and cook meat and other foods. Insulation held the heat so that night cooking was done. As it was necessary to turn the mirror from east to west daily, a simple clockwork governed by an alarm clock was provided for that purpose.

Another machine used three unit mirrors mounted in a frame with their axes east-west, the frame being rotated to follow the march of the sun. The heated liquid from all three mirrors was circulated through well-insulated tubes to a steam boiler above, where steam was raised at 175 pounds pressure to the square inch, sufficient for one-half horsepower. Said Dr. Abbot:

"About 15 percent of the solar energy received by the three mirrors may be converted into mechanical work. It is well known that the wasted solar energy in deserts is thousands of times more than all the power requirements of the world. If this energy could be maintained constantly without interruption it could be made to compete on equal terms with coal at about $3 a ton. It must be remembered that solar radiation is interrupted by night and by clouds. An efficient power or heat storage would have to be provided if large solar power plants were to be used."

Secretary

DR. ABBOT was the logical choice as Walcott's successor in 1927. He had grown up in the Institution and had already been Assistant Secretary for ten years. Furthermore, he represented the physical sciences, and in accordance with Smithsonian tradition the new Secretary should be a physicist. His standing as a scientist was pre-eminent; he had served for five years (1918-23) as home secretary of the National Academy of Sciences, was the author of many scientific papers in astrophysics and astronomy, and had traveled widely. He was made Secretary on January 10, 1928, under auspices that promised great things for the Institution, for the campaign had just been launched to increase the Smithsonian endowment.

But then came the depression. Some of the investments of the Institution became less productive, Governmental appropriations and salaries were cut, and support for science dwindled. Many of the Smithsonian's activities had to mark time, but there were some compensations. For one thing, under the stimulus and promotion of Dr. William M. Mann, energetic director of the National Zoological Park, the Federal W.P.A. building program made funds available for some badly needed buildings at the Zoo. At a total cost of $1,298,000 there were built a new reptile house, a wing on the bird house, a small-mammal house, a central heating plant, and shops, which made the facilities at the National Zoo adequate and attractive. In addition, several notable gifts came to the Institution. One of these was the large art collection of John Gellatly, valued at $4,500,000, which is now a part of the National Collection of Fine Arts and exhibited in its entirety in the Natural History Building.

To Diffuse Knowledge

WE HAVE MENTIONED in earlier chapters many of the publications that the Smithsonian has issued in its program of diffusing knowledge. During Dr. Abbot's secretaryship this phase of the Institution's work was dominant in spite of ever-restricted printing funds.

The magnitude of Smithsonian publications has always been remarkable in view of the modest income available. *The Smithsonian Annual Reports,* each containing an appendix which is virtually a yearbook of contemporary science, now number a hundred volumes and constitute altogether a scientific compendium perhaps unmatched anywhere. Since the establishment of the Smithsonian thirty-five volumes of the *Contributions to Knowledge* and over a hundred volumes of the *Smithsonian Miscellaneous Collections* have been issued, containing hundreds of original papers in the arts and sciences. Two hundred *Bulletins of the National Museum* (some in several volumes) have appeared; 100 volumes of Museum *Proceedings;* 150 *Bulletins of the Bureau of American Ethnology;* 30 volumes of *Contributions from the National Herbarium;* and many others. There are series within series—for example Ridgway's "Birds of North and Middle America," Bent's "Life Histories of North American Birds," the monumental handbooks of North American and South American Indians, and the Smithsonian physical, meteorological, and mathematical tables. Various individual author-scientists have contributed large portions of their life-work to Smithsonian publications; for example, Aleš Hrdlička's monographs on Early Man and his measurements of human crania; Dr. Walcott's long series of papers on new discoveries in Cambrian and pre-Cambrian geology; R. E. Snodgrass's notable contributions to the anatomy of insects; Dr. John R. Swanton's works in ethnology; H. H. Clayton's world weather records; and Dr. Abbot's many papers on solar radiation and its relation to terrestrial weather.

Indeed, Dr. Abbot's own publications through the years have been impressive. In addition to scores of shorter technical papers, his most assiduous work for the Smithsonian is contained in five volumes of the *Annals of the Astrophysical Observatory,* which embrace the official results of the Observatory's research and are regarded as classic work on the whole subject of solar radiation and variation. In 1911 he published his book *The Sun,* in which he advocated the theory, now accepted but then revolutionary, that the photosphere of the sun was not a cloud of liquid particles, as was generally believed, but entirely gaseous. A new and improved edition of this volume came out in 1929. *The Earth and the Stars,* a popular astronomy, first appeared in 1925; a revised edition was published in 1947. He also wrote *Every Day Mysteries,* twenty scientific stories for young people.

A unique publishing venture that came to fruition during Dr. Abbot's regime was inaugurated by the Institution about 1925. It was arranged to produce a series of popular books on science, to be written by members or associates of the Smithsonian staff but to be published and marketed by a New York publishing corporation, with royalties to be paid to the Institution. Dr. Abbot assumed the general editorship of the series (known as the "Smithsonian Scientific Series") and himself wrote two of the volumes—*The Sun and the Welfare of Man* and *Great Inventions.* These dozen books have proved so extremely successful that to date the Institution has realized in the neighborhood of half a million dollars (about $25,000 a year) from the royalties.

Another far-reaching means of diffusing knowledge, encouraged by Dr. Abbot, was the Smithsonian's nationwide radio program known as "The World Is Yours," which for six years was broadcast weekly over a wide network of the National Broadcasting Company. Produced in dramatized form, in cooperation with the United States Office of Education, the programs covered in some way virtually every department of human knowledge. They were tremendously popular and were terminated only because of the pressure for air time during World War II. Never before had the Smithsonian Institution reached so many people.

Also particularly gratifying to Secretary Abbot was an almost fabulous art benefaction that came to the Nation during his term of office. This was Andrew W. Mellon's gift of his unexcelled art collection and a $15,000,000 gallery. It was to be known as the National Gallery of Art and administered by a separate Board of Trustees but as a bureau of the Smithsonian Institution. The building was completed and opened to the public in 1941, and immediately took its place as one of the great galleries of the world. Besides the nucleus collection—111 choice old masters and 21 pieces of sculpture comprising Mr. Mellon's initial gift—numerous other valuable private collections have been added. Among these are the large collection of Italian paintings and sculpture given by Samuel H. Kress, the priceless Widener and Chester Dale collections, and several thousand prints given by Lessing J. Rosenwald. And more are being added yearly. This new National Gallery, together with the Freer Gallery of Art and the National Collection of Fine Arts, has made the Smithsonian one of the leading centers in the world for the study and enjoyment of art, a consummation that seems quite in harmony with the dream of James Smithson.

The Smithsonian at War

AT THE BEGINNING of 1942 the Smithsonian found itself in a difficult position. The country had been plunged into a dual war against Germany and Japan, and the Government was mobilizing its all-out war effort. What could an agency like the Smithsonian do best?—an agency for a hundred years dedicated to high-minded scientific research regardless of its "palpable utility," as Joseph Henry put it. Dr. Abbot knew that this war was to be pre-eminently a scientist's war. He also knew that the sciences dealt in at the Smithsonian—mainly anthropology, biology, geology, and astrophysics—were not the obvious military sciences. The Institution's facilities consisted of museums, art galleries, small laboratories, and a highly specialized staff, not of rich factories of industrial research, atomic physicists, or warfare chemists. Yet ever since the time when Joseph Henry had been Abraham Lincoln's adviser during the Civil War, the Smithsonian had participated as best it could in the nation's military conflicts, and World War II could be no exception.

Dr. Abbot therefore appointed a War Committee to canvass the possibilities of what the Institution could do and to recommend definite lines of action. The results were noteworthy. As stated in a brief summary of this wartime activity in the 1945 Smithsonian *Report,* "a large part of the effort of the staff was diverted to work connected directly or indirectly with the war, and the Smithsonian Institution was found to be an essential cog in the great war machine in Washington. Although its role was inconspicuous as compared with those of the large war agencies, nevertheless it was found to offer services not readily available elsewhere—services whose lack might well have led to costly mistakes and delays."

One project that attracted wide attention was the publication of the "War Background Studies," a series of illustrated booklets on the peoples, geography, history, natural history, and other features of the far-flung parts of the earth to which the war reached, especially in the Pacific area. Twenty-one numbers of the Studies were issued, and at the end of the war over 630,000 copies had been printed, including 400,000 copies especially for the Army and Navy. Another project was the preparation for the

U. S. Navy of a manual, *Survival on Land and Sea,* which was widely distributed to members of the armed forces.

The Institution also served during this period as one of the sponsors of the Ethnogeographic Board, a joint non-governmental agency created by the National Research Council, the American Council of Learned Societies, the Social Science Research Council, and the Smithsonian Institution as a means of bringing together all the known resources of specialized and regional knowledge urgently needed by the armed forces. Liaison with the armed forces was established through officers details especially for this service. This Board functioned efficiently throughout the war with offices in the Smithsonian Building and with Smithsonian members on its staff.

During the war years the United States Government, through the State Department, undertook a special program of cultural and scientific cooperation with the American Republics, in response to the growing sense of a need for greater understanding among all the American peoples. As a part of this program there was created in 1943, as an agency of the Smithsonian, the Institute of Social Anthropology. The work of the Institute has two objectives: (1) to introduce modern social-science theories and techniques to other countries so that they may train their own scholars for such work, and (2) to accumulate basic social-science data about the rural populations in those countries. Dr. Abbot appointed Dr. Julian H. Steward as the first director of the Institute, whose operations opened a promising new field for Smithsonian leadership.

In 1897 Dr. Abbot was married to Lillian Elvira Moore, of Virginia. Mrs. Abbot, who died in 1944, was a talented artist. Their home in Washington was a delightful spot, and the two often entertained the Abracadabra Club, a local group of amateur musicians, artists, and writers. Dr. Abbot is fond of music and enjoys playing the cello. He

takes delight in amusing his friends with songs and hu-
morous recitations. He likes simplicity and plain people,
and has a knack for seeing through sham and pomposity.
He has enlivened many a too-serious conference with an
Abbotesque anecdote, and has even employed an occasional song to rout the deadliness of officialdom. Many
have counted the friendship of Charles Greeley Abbot as
one of their richest experiences. Like many New England-
ers, he does not waste words, and tends to be gnomic of
utterance and philosophical of temperament. He is a
staunch Republican, proud of his New Hampshire ancestry. For many years he has been an active member of
the Congregational Church and in past years frequently
spoke from the pulpit on some religious-scientific subject,
many of his "sermons" appearing in pamphlet form. In
his younger days he was a tennis player and for many
years he has been an ardent golfer.

Dr. Abbot has remarked that his ideal aim as Secretary
was to follow the policies laid down by Joseph Henry,
namely: to make the attainment of new knowledge and
its diffusion by publication the primary thing; to coop-
erate with scholars and learned societies here and abroad
in all worthy efforts to advance knowledge; and to re-
linquish to other agencies fields adequately covered by
them.

While Assistant Secretary, he was much impressed by
a saying of Secretary Walcott: "Do things! If you are
right 75 percent of the time, that is a good batting average. Do not hesitate to act after due deliberation." And
at another time: "If you want someone to do something
for you, state it briefly and clearly, and have it prepared
so that he has only to sign on the dotted line."

As has been mentioned in the previous chapter, Dr.
Abbot devoted much effort to settling the lamentable
controversy with Orville Wright over the disposition of
the Wright plane.

Over the years honors and degrees have come to Dr.
Abbot from many scientific societies and universities in

recognition of his achievements in astronomy, but the greatest honor, he would tell you, was that of being fifth in line after Joseph Henry as Secretary of the Smithsonian Institution. On June 30, 1944, he resigned and was given the title of research associate, with the privilege of remaining as long as he wished to carry on his work at the Observatory without administrative burdens to interfere.

An Ornithologist as Secretary

THE MAN named as Abbot's successor was Alexander Wetmore, who had been Assistant Secretary of the Smithsonian and Director of the National Museum since 1925. Dr. Wetmore's appointment in several ways marked a milestone in Smithsonian history. In the first place, the end of the war came soon afterward, which meant that the Institution would resume its peacetime programs. In the second place, it nearly coincided with the one-hundredth anniversary of the founding of the Institution. In the third place, a new epoch in science, the Atomic Age, had dawned for the world, challenging every scientist and scientific establishment worthy of the name.

Dr. Wetmore came to the secretaryship with a brilliant career in biology. When he became Secretary he had already had more than thirty years of experience in scientific work in the Government. He was born on June 18, 1886, at North Freedom, Wis., and as a small boy developed a precocious interest in natural history. Before he was twenty years old he had his first museum job, as assistant at the University of Kansas Museum. In 1910 he took his first Government position, that of agent for the Biological Survey, then a bureau of the United States Department of Agriculture. After receiving his A.B. degree from the University of Kansas in 1912, he was promoted to assistant biologist with the Survey and went to Washington, where he began to work in the Survey's studies of the food habits of North American birds. He enjoyed his work, for his chief interest was birds, and the training in economic ornithology proved fruitful. Furthermore, being in Washington enabled him to associate with such Government naturalists as E. W. Nelson, C. Hart Merriam, A. K. Fisher, Leonhard Stejneger, Charles W. Richmond, and Robert Ridgway, with and under whom it was a rare privilege for a young man to study.

He continued his academic studies, too, and in 1916 took an M. S. degree and in 1920 a Ph. D. from George Washington University. Washington and the East also offered exceptional opportunities for descriptive ornithology, with the great bird collections of the National Museum, the Museum of Comparative Zoology, the American Museum of Natural History, and the Academy of Natural Sciences of Philadelphia. Dr. Wetmore took full advantage of these facilities and rapidly became one of the leading ornithological authorities of the world, especially upon avian anatomy and osteology, fossil birds, bird migration, and the taxonomy of birds. Whenever possible he supplemented his laboratory research by field work. In 1911 he went to Puerto Rico to spend nearly a year studying the birdlife of that and adjacent islands. In 1920 he was sent to South America to study the birds that migrate into the southern part of that continent, and in 1923 he was head of the *Tanager* exploring expedition to the mid-Pacific sponsored by the U. S. Biological Survey and the Bishop Museum of Honolulu. Between whiles his investigations took him into most of the forty-eight states, as well as to parts of Alaska and southern Canada. In more recent years he has carried on natural-history explorations in many parts of the world—particularly in Spain, Hispaniola, Guatemala, Venezuela, Mexico, Cost Rica, Colombia, and Panama.

In November 1924, Ned Hollister, superintendent of the National Zoological Park, died suddenly, and Dr. Wetmore was named by Dr. Walcott as Hollister's successor. The position was short-lived, however, for the following March Walcott made him Assistant Secretary of the Smithsonian, with direct charge of the National

Museum. This post he held for almost twenty years, during which time he administered the National Museum along conservative principles, fostered its researches in laboratory and in the field on a broad base, and continued to build up its collections in natural history, anthropology, and industrial arts that had been initiated by Baird and Goode. He gave special encouragement to fundamental research by the Museum staff and expanded the activities to the extent that available funds would allow.

In addition to his administrative duties, he continued to enhance his international reputation as an ornithologist and brought out a number of important works: *Observations on the Birds of Argentina, Paraguay, Uruguay, and Chile* (1926), *The Migration of Birds* (1927), *Birds of Porto Rico and the Virgin Islands* (1928), *Birds of Haiti and the Dominican Republic* (1931), and *Fossil Birds of North America* (1931). He also proposed and published a *Systematic Classification for the Birds of the World,* which has found wide acceptance among bird authorities, and wrote large parts of the two-volume *Books of Birds,* issued in 1937 by the National Geographic Society. In 1940 Dr. Wetmore was made secretary-general of the Eighth American Scientific Congress which met in Washington that year. This was the largest conference of its series ever held up to that time and brought him into contact with most of the leading scientists of North and South America. He has also served as president of the American Ornithologists' Union (an organization in which he has been particularly active), the Washington Academy of Sciences, the Cosmos Club of Washington, the Explorer's Club of New York, the Biological Society of Washington, the Baird Ornithological Club, and the Washington Biologists' Field Club, and is named as president for the Tenth International Ornithological Congress. He is a trustee and vice-chairman of the Research Committee of the National Geographic Society and a member of the American Committee, International Wildlife Protection, chairman of the Advisory Board of the National

Air Museum; and a member of the Board of Trustees of George Washington University.

It is noteworthy that two Smithsonian Secretaries, Baird and Wetmore, chose ornithology as their life work. Since the time of Aristotle the study of birds has attracted not only professional naturalists but also countless amateurs —Pliny the Elder; Frederick II, Holy Roman emperor, whose work on falconry is classic; Conrad Gesner; Gilbert White of Selborne; John James Audubon; Charles Lucien Bonaparte; Lord Grey of Fallodon; Theodore Roosevelt— to cite a few familiar names among both categories. In the United States today it runs a close race with stamp collecting as a popular avocation. Franklin Delano Roosevelt was both a philatelist and an amateur ornithologist, and was an associate member of the American Ornithologists' Union for forty-nine years. Dr. Wetmore is able to enrich the study of both amateur and professional: he is recognized by his scientific colleagues as one of the world's leading ornithologists, and through his popular writings and associations is held high in the estimation of thousands of less professional bird students of all ages throughout America.

Dr. Wetmore finds his recreation mainly outdoors, principally studying birds afield, tracing the distribution of various forms of birdlife in areas nearby Washington, delighting in their interesting habits and mannerisms, and above all in evaluating their adjustments to the varying environments in which they are found. In this his aim is to spend at least one day a week outdoors, combining with his natural-history observations such other activities as driving, walking, canoeing, and swimming. His work hours are long—two hours or so in early morning devoted to writing and laboratory research before the offices are open, a full day of appointments and administration, and then another hour or two of study in the evening. His writing is done in these earlier and later hours. Holidays from administration are given to field investigations and expeditions, mainly in Latin America, which serve not only as a source of collections and observations for his writings, but also as a means of keeping him in touch with travel and work conditions in connection with the considerable field program that he sponsors and administers.

Dr. Wetmore was married in 1912 to Fay Holloway, of Kansas. For many years they have made their home in Takoma Park, in suburban Washington. They have a married daughter.

In February 1948 President Truman appointed Dr. Wetmore chairman of the Interdepartmental Committee on Research and Development, which had been created the previous December following a careful study of the need of an organized correlation of the Nation's scientific research. Of this appointment the *Washington Evening Star* commented editorially: "Dr. Wetmore's training and practice would mean little were they not supported by a natural talent for getting along with people. His statesmanship is a notable asset in relation to the job to which the President has named him. Thirteen other Government officers are to serve with him, and each one of them represents qualities of distinction. Beyond them, however, are hundreds if not thousands of men and women, each engaged in a scientific task of importance to the security and prosperity of the national community. The committee is pledged to 'the promotion of the national welfare' in the full and complete meaning of the phrase. It will seek an effective correlation of research effort wherever it may be going forward."

But the story of Dr. Wetmore's career as Secretary of the Smithsonian Institution we must leave to future historians, for as this is written he has held that office less than four years. One of his first tasks as Secretary was to direct the return of Smithsonian activities to their prewar peacetime basis, following considerable reductions in staff and in purchasing power of funds for operation incident to the war period. At the same time various administrative procedures of the Institution required readjustment.

Plans had to be formulated for celebrating the Smithsonian Centenary, although postwar conditions prevented making the celebration as elaborate as it deserved to be. In the late summer and autumn of 1946 the occasion was appropriately observed. The Post Office Department issued a special United States three-cent postage stamp showing the old brownstone Smithsonian Building in full-front view, with James Smithson's words FOR THE INCREASE AND DIFFUSION OF KNOWLEDGE AMONG MEN across the sky. Special publications were issued, including a finely printed booklet, *The First Hundred Years of the Smithsonian Institution,* prepared by Webster P. True and widely distributed throughout the country. A convocation of scientists and a gala reception were held. For the new Secretary the Centennial offered a timely opportunity for a backward look—to review a full century of Smithsonian history, to note where it had failed and where it might have done better, to rejoice in its successes and achievements, to do honor to its great men. And then—to look to the future.

CHRONOLOGY OF PRINCIPAL EVENTS IN SMITHSONIAN HISTORY

[The first fifty years of this Chronology are adapted from Goode, 1897 (see Bibliography)]

1826

Oct. 23. James Smithson's will made.

1829

June 27. Death of James Smithson in Genoa, Italy.

1835

July 28. United States Government advised that it was entitled to bequest of Smithson.

1836

Nov. 14. Richard Rush, as agent for United States, entered suit in British Court of Chancery to obtain possession of the bequest.

1838

May 9. Chancery suit decided in favor of United States.

Sept. 1. Bequest deposited in United States Mint in Philadelphia.

1846

Aug. 10. Act of Congress organizing Smithsonian Institution approved by President Polk.

Sept. 7. First meeting of Board of Regents held; George M. Dallas elected Chancellor.

Dec. 3. Joseph Henry elected Secretary.

Dec. 4. Board of Regents adopted a plan of organization.

1847

May 1. Cornerstone of Smithsonian Building laid.

1848

July 1. System of meteorological observations established, in connection with which Secretary Henry proposed that the magnetic telegraph be used in investigating atmospheric phenomena, and that notice of approaching storms be given to distant observers.

Dec. 1. First volume of *Smithsonian Contributions to Knowledge* published and distributed.

1849

April 30. System of international exchanges inaugurated.

June 27. Appropriation made for collections in natural history.

1850

Jan. 22. Explorations under auspices of the Institution, or aided by its funds, instituted, especially in Oregon, California, and Mexico.

July 5. Spencer Fullerton Baird appointed Assistant Secretary.

1853

Feb. 3. Magnetic observatory on Smithsonian grounds authorized by Board of Regents.

1854

December. Main portion of Smithsonian Building completed.

1855

March 3. *Annual Report* for 1854 ordered by Congress, being the first to contain the Smithsonian lectures, extracts from correspondence, and miscellaneous papers in the form of a General Appendix.

1857

March 31. Personal effects of James Smithson removed from Patent Office and deposited in Regents' room at the Institution.

1858

Aug. 8. Daily weather-map, from telegraphic reports received every morning, exhibited in Smithsonian Building.

1860

Dec. 31. Magnetic observatory discontinued.

1861

June 13. Balloons sent up from Smithsonian grounds by Thaddeus S. C. Lowe, to test practicability of their employment for military purposes.

1862

June 2. Series of publications called *Smithsonian Miscellaneous Collections* begun.

1865

Jan. 24. Fire destroyed principal part of contents of the rooms in upper story of Smithsonian Building and adjacent towers, including personal effects of Smithson.

1866

April 5. Act passed by Congress transferring custody of Smithsonian Library to Library of Congress.

1867

March 2. Act passed by Congress to provide for fifty copies of all documents printed by either House of Congress, or by any Department or Bureau, to be exchanged through the agency of the Smithsonian for similar works published in foreign countries, and especially by foreign governments.

1868

Jan. 1. National Herbarium transferred to Department of Agriculture.

1869

July 7. West range of Smithsonian Building, in addition to the main halls, assigned to the use of the Museum.

1871

Feb. 25. Assistant Secretary Spencer F. Baird appointed United States Commissioner of Fish and Fisheries by President Grant.

March 3. Appropriation made by Congress for continuing survey of Colorado River by John W. Powell, under direction of Secretary of Smithsonian.

1872

June 8. Law passed that publications marked "Smithsonian exchanges" should be allowed to pass free in the mail.

1873

Dec. 31. Smithsonian meteorological work transferred to Signal Service, War Department.

1874

Feb. 13. Paintings, statuary, engravings, and books on art belonging to Institution deposited in Corcoran Art Gallery.

1875

Nov. 23. A series of publications entitled *Bulletins of the United States National Museum* begun.

1876

May 10 to Nov. 10. Smithsonian participated in Centennial Exposition in Philadelphia.

1878

May 13. Death of Secretary Joseph Henry.

May 17. Spencer F. Baird elected Secretary.

1879

March 3. Congress appropriated $250,000 for a fireproof building for the National Museum.

March 3. All official mail matter sent from Smithsonian allowed transmission free of postage by Act of Congress.

March 3. Congress ordered "all collections of rocks, minerals, soils, fossils, and objects of natural history, archeology and ethnology made by the Coast and Interior Survey, the Geological Survey, or by any other parties for the Government of the United States, when no longer needed for investigations in progress, to be deposited in the National Museum."

March 3. Congress ordered "all the archives, records, and materials relating to the Indians of North America, collected by the Geographical and Geological Survey of the Rocky Mountain Region, turned over to the Smithsonian Institution, that the work may be completed and prepared for publication under its direction."

July 3. Secretary Baird designated John W. Powell to take charge of the ethnological work, as provided by Congresss.

Aug. 1. Series of publications entitled *Proceedings of the National Museum* begun.

1880

June 14. Congress ordered first report of Bureau of Ethnology to be published.

1881

October. National Museum Building occupied.

1883

Apr. 19. Bronze statue of Joseph Henry, by W. W. Story, erected in Smithsonian grounds, unveiled.

1884

July 5. Franking privilege extended to all official mail matter of Smithsonian Institution by order of Congress.

1887

Jan. 12. George Brown Goode and Samuel P. Langley appointed Assistant Secretaries.

July 7. Director of National Museum directed to report annually to Congress on the progress and condition of the Museum.

Aug. 19. Death of Secretary Spencer F. Baird.

Nov. 18. Samuel P. Langley elected Secretary.

1889

Jan. 4. American Historical Association incorporated by Congress and directed to report annually to Secretary of Smithsonian.

March 2. National Zoological Park established by Act of Congress.

1890

March 1. Astrophysical Observatory started in wooden building on Smithsonian grounds.

April 30. National Zoological Park placed under direction of Regents of Smithsonian by order of Congress.

1891

March 3. First Congressional appropriation ($10,000) made for maintenance of Astrophysical Observatory.

Sept. 22. Gift of $200,000 from Thomas G. Hodgkins, half to be used for "the investigation of the properties of atmospheric air."

1893

Jan. 25. New Smithsonian seal, designed by Augustus St. Gaudens, adopted.

March 31. Announcement of establishment of Hodgkins prizes and medal.

1894

July 28. National Herbarium recalled from Department of Agriculture.

Sept. 12. Death of Robert Stanton Avery, who bequeathed his property ($35,000) to the Institution.

1895

Dec. 25. Complete set of Smithsonian publications deposited in Library of Pembroke College, Oxford, the college from which James Smithson was graduated.

1896

May 6. Successful flight of Langley's model aerodrome, a "mechanism, built chiefly of steel and driven by a steam engine," weighing 26 pounds.

July 18. Paintings, engravings, and other art works, deposited in Corcoran Gallery of Art in 1874 and later, returned at request of Regents.

Sept. 6. Death of George Brown Goode, Assistant Secretary.

Nov. 18. Bronze tablet directed to be placed on Smithson's tomb by the Institution, and a replica in the English Church in Genoa, Italy.

Nov. 28. Successful trial of Langley's Model Aerodrome No. 6, demonstrating the practicability of mechanical flight, which had been long debated and discredited.

1897

Feb. 1. Richard Rathbun appointed Assistant Secretary.

July 1. National Museum reorganization effected, whereby the various divisions were placed under three departments with three scientific men in charge as head curators.

1899

Feb. 20. First report of Daughters of the American Revolution transmitted to Congress by Secretary of Smithsonian, in accordance with law approved February 20, 1896.

1900

June 12-13. Third and final conference on International Catalogue of Scientific Literature held in London.

June 19. First volume of *Annals of the Astrophysical Observatory* issued.

1901

Jan. 23. Joseph White Sprague bequeathed to the Institution about 40 per cent of his estate (estimated at $200,000), to be known as the "Sprague Fund."

1902

May. First annual issue of the *International Catalogue of Scientific Literature* released.

Sept. 15. Addison T. Reid died, leaving an estate of about $10,000 to the Institution to found a chair in biology in memory of his grandfather, Asher Tunis.

Sept. 23. Maj. John W. Powell, director of the Bureau of Ethnology, died.

Oct. 11. William Henry Holmes appointed chief of the Bureau of Ethnology.

1903

March 3. Congress provided funds for a new National Museum building, cost not to exceed $3,500,000.

Oct. 7 and Dec. 8. Secretary Langley unsuccessfully attempted to launch his large man-carrying aerodrome.

1905

March 6. Cyrus Adler appointed Assistant Secretary.

March 6. Tomb and remains of James Smithson, brought from Italy, installed in mortuary chapel in Smithsonian Building.

Dec. 15. Charles L. Freer, Detroit, Mich., offered his entire art collection to the Smithsonian Institution or to the United States Government.

1906

Jan. 24. Gift of Charles L. Freer accepted by Board of Regents—his art collection and $500,000 for a building in which to house it.

Feb. 27. Death of Secretary Samuel P. Langley.

June 30. International Catalogue of Scientific Literature received its first Congressional appropriation—$5,000.

July 11. Supreme Court of the District of Columbia decreed that the collection of art contemplated in the act of establishment of the Smithsonian Institution was within the meaning and intent of the law the National Gallery of Art, thereby enabling the Harriet Lane Johnston art collection to become the property of the Institution.

Dec. 4. Henry Fairfield Osborn elected Secretary but declined.

1907

Jan. 23. Charles Doolittle Walcott elected Secretary.

March 1. Charles Greeley Abbot appointed director of Astrophysical Observatory.

1908

Apr. 16. Advisory Committee of five artists formed to decide upon standard of merit in acceptance of works for National Gallery of Art.

Dec. 15. Langley medal established, for "specially meritorious investigations in connection with the science of aerodromics and its application to aviation."

1909

Feb. 10. Wilbur and Orville Wright awarded the Langley medal.

March 23. Expedition headed by Theodore Roosevelt sailed for Africa, under auspices of the Smithsonian; it made important additions to the biological collections.

December. Institution agreed to undertake publication of the *Opinions of the International Commission on Zoological Nomenclature.*

1910

Jan. 1. William H. Holmes resigned as chief of Bureau of Ethnology to become curator of National Gallery of Art and the National Museum's head curator of anthropology; Frederick W. Hodge appointed to succeed him.

March 17. Part of new Natural History Building opened to public at an informal opening of National Gallery of Art.

Dec. 28. Biological survey of the Canal Zone begun, "to cover studies of the animal and plant life of the land and waters of the Canal Zone" before the fauna became obliterated by joining of oceans by construction of the Canal.

1911

Feb. 9. Regents informed that the Institution had inherited from Lucy T. and George W. Poore an estate estimated at $40,000.

June 1. Frederick W. True appointed Assistant Secretary.

June 20. All structural work on the Natural History Building completed.

Aug. 18. Publication of the "Langley Memoir on Mechanical Flight."

1912

Feb. 16. Research Corporation of New York organized, for the management of patents "relating to the electrical precipitation of dust, smoke, and chemical fumes," presented to the Institution by Dr. Frederick G. Cottrell.

Oct. 8. Death of Morris Loeb, who made the Institution a residual legatee of his estate "for the furtherance of knowledge in the exact sciences."

1913

Feb. 13. Langley medal awarded to Glenn H. Curtiss and to Gustave Eiffel.

May 1. Regents approve plan to reopen the Langley Aerodynamical Laboratory and to appoint an Advisory Committee.

May 6. Langley memorial tablet unveiled in the Smithsonian Building, the anniversary of the successful flight of the model aerodrome in 1896.

May 9. Death of Leander T. Chamberlain, who bequeathed to the Institution $25,000, to be known as the Frances Lea Chamberlain fund for "promoting the increase, and the scientific value and usefulness," of the Isaac Lea collection of gems and gem material, and an additional $10,000 to be used "for promoting the scientific value and usefulness" of the Isaac Lea collection of mollusks.

1915

March 3. National Advisory Committee for Aeronautics established; Secretary Walcott elected chairman of the executive committee.

Dec. 4. Charles L. Freer donated $1,000,000 for immediate erection of the Freer Gallery of Art, waiving the condition that the collection was to stay in his possession during his lifetime.

1916

June 19. National Research Council organized, with Secretary Walcott as a vice chairman of the executive committee.

Nov. 1. Frank Baker resigned as Superintendent of National Zoological Park; Ned Hollister appointed to succeed him.

1918

March 1. Frederick W. Hodge, ethnologist-in-charge of the Bureau of American Ethnology, resigned; J. Walter Fewkes appointed chief.

July 16. At the request of the President of the United States the Natural History Building closed to the public and all the exhibition halls turned over to the Bureau of War Risk Insurance for office space.

Dec. 16. Charles G. Abbot appointed Assistant Secretary.

1919

Apr. 14. $50,000 bequeathed by Mrs. Virginia Purdy Bacon to establish the Walter Rathbone Bacon Traveling Scholarship for the study of the faunas of countries other than the United States.

1920

May & June. John A. Roebling started a series of contributions for the work of Astrophysical Observatory, the first of which was $11,000.

July 1. National Gallery of Art made an independent bureau, with William H. Holmes as Director.

Oct. 7. Aircraft Building opened to the public.

Dec. 1. John Ellerton Lodge appointed curator of Freer Gallery of Art.

1921

Apr. 30. Freer Gallery of Art Building completed.

June 30. Printing of the International Catalogue of Scientific Literature suspended.

1922

June 6. The Charles D. and Mary Vaux Walcott research fund of $11,520 established.

1924

Apr. 9. First Smithsonian broadcast went on the air.

Nov. 3. Death of Ned Hollister. Alexander Wetmore appointed to succeed him as Superintendent of National Zoological Park.

1925

March. National Geographic Society made a grant of $55,000 to select a site for and to equip a solar-radiation station in the Eastern Hemisphere.

April 1. Alexander Wetmore appointed Assistant Secretary in charge of the National Museum.

May 13. William M. Mann appointed superintendent of National Zoological Park.

November. Regents announced opening of a drive to raise $10,000,000 for Institution's endowment fund.

1926

July 13. Frederick A. Canfield died, bequeathing to the Smithsonian his large collection of precious mineralogical specimens, with an endowment of $50,000 for its care and development.

Dec. 14. An agreement entered into with a New York publisher to start work on the "Smithsonian Scientific Series."

1927

Feb. 9. Death of Secretary Charles Doolittle Walcott.

Feb. 10. John A. Roebling, in memory of his father, Col. Washington A. Roebling, conveyed to the Smithsonian the Roebling collection of minerals and gems and established the Roebling fund of $150,000 for its care and development.

Feb. 11. Conference held on the future policy of the Institution.

June 11. Langley medal awarded to Charles A. Lindbergh.

1928

Jan. 10. Charles G. Abbot elected Secretary.

Jan. 15. J. Walter Fewkes retired as chief of the Bureau of American Ethnology.

Aug. 1. Matthew W. Stirling appointed to succeed Dr. Fewkes.

1929

June 6. Congress passed a bill requesting the Institution to thank John Gellatly for gift of his art collection and authorizing appropriations for its maintenance.

Oct. 17. Death of William H. Rollins, who bequeathed $53,-580 to the Institution to establish a fund to be known as "the Miriam and William Rollins Fund for Exploration Beyond the Boundary of Knowledge."

Dec. 12. Langley medal awarded to Charles M. Manly (posthumously) and to Admiral Richard E. Byrd.

1930

Apr. 27. Death of James Arthur, who willed $75,000 to the Smithsonian for investigation and study of the sun and for providing annually a lecture to be known as the James Arthur Annual Lecture on the Sun.

1931

Oct. 5. Regent Dwight W. Morrow died, bequeathing $100,000 to Smithsonian endowment fund.

1933

March 13. Adolph M. Hanson executed a legal assignment to the Institution of all royalties accruing under a patent on his discovery, the isolation of the parathyroid hormone.

June 30. Work of the *International Catalogue of Scientific Literature* suspended.

1935

Jan. 17. Langley medal awarded to Joseph S. Ames.

Jan. 26. Allotment of $680,000 from the Public Works Administration made for the erection of a small-mammal house, a pachyderm house, an addition to the bird house, and mechanical shops at National Zoological Park.

1936

Apr. 2. A bequest of approximately $100,000 received from William L. Abbott.

June 7. In cooperation with the Office of Education, Department of the Interior, Smithsonian radio program, "The World is Yours," inaugurated—a series of weekly half-hour nation-wide broadcasts.

Dec. 31. Andrew W. Mellon gave to the American people his art collection, a $10,000,000 building to exhibit it, and an endowment fund for salaries and the acquisition of additional art works, the gallery to be a bureau of the Smithsonian Institution but administered by its own board of trustees.

1937

Mar. 24. The name of the National Gallery of Art changed to the National Collection of Fine Arts, and the name National Gallery of Art given to the new Mellon gallery.

1938

Dec. 20. Annie-May Hegeman, as a memorial to her father, Henry Kirke Porter, offered the Institution half the proceeds of the sale of her property, amounting to approximately $600,000.

1939

June 29. Prizes awarded in the competition for a Smithsonian Gallery of Art Building; first prize of $7,500 awarded to Eliel Saarinen.

1940

May 17. Approximately $130,000 received from the estate of Eleanor E. Witherspoon to found the Thomas W. Witherspoon Memorial on condition that none of the income therefrom should be used in collecting birds and animals dead or alive or for purposes of vivisection.

Aug. 22. Through the death of Mary Vaux Walcott the Institution received $400,000, to be added to the Charles D. and Mary Vaux Walcott Research Fund.

Dec. 10. National Gallery of Art Building completed at a cost of approximately $15,000,000.

1941

Jan. 20. A new exhibit to serve as a visual index to all Smithsonian activities, in the great hall of the Smithsonian Building, opened to the public.

Mar. 17. The National Gallery of Art Building opened to the public.

1942

Apr. 1. A War Committee formed to recommend methods of participation by the Institution in the war effort.

May 10. "The World is Yours" radio program terminated.

June 10. The first paper in the Smithsonian's "War Background Studies" published.

Dec. 29. Death of John E. Lodge, Director of Freer Gallery of Art.

1943

Jan. 16. Archibald G. Wenley named Director of Freer Gallery of Art.

May. Ethnogeographic Board organized under the joint auspices of the Smithsonian Institution, the American Council of Learned Societies, the Social Science Research Council, and the National Research Council, with offices in the Smithsonian Building.

Sept. 1. Julian H. Steward appointed Director of the Institute of Social Anthropology, an autonomous unit of the Bureau of American Ethnology.

1944

June 30. Charles G. Abbot resigned as Secretary.

1945

Jan. 12. Alexander Wetmore elected Secretary.

Apr. 1. John E. Graf appointed Assistant Secretary.

Apr. 16. Loyal B. Aldrich named Director of Astrophysical Observatory.

Oct. 9. Secretary of the Interior authorized a cooperative project between the Smithsonian Institution and the National Park Service, with Frank H. H. Roberts, Jr., as Director; the project was to be known as the River Basin Surveys, to determine the extent and nature of archeological and paleontological remains occurring in areas to be flooded by the construction of dams by the Bureau of Reclamation and the Corps of Engineers, U. S. Army.

1946

July 16. Canal Zone Biological Area placed under the administration of the Institution.

July 28. Ruel P. Tolman named Director of National Collection of Fine Arts.

Aug. 10. The 100th anniversary of the Smithsonian celebrated, and a commemorative postage stamp issued for the occasion.

Aug. 12. By Act of Congress, National Air Museum established under the Smithsonian Institution.

Sept. 3. Dr. Steward resigned as Director of the Institute of Social Anthropology; succeeded by George M. Foster.

1947

Feb. 25. John L. Keddy appointed Assistant Secretary.

1948

Feb. 14. Secretary Wetmore appointed Chairman of the Interdepartmental Committee on Research and Development.

Apr. 1. Thomas M. Beggs named Director of National Collection of Fine Arts, succeeding Mr. Tolman, retired.

May 26. A. Remington Kellogg appointed Director of the United States National Museum.

SELECTED BIBLIOGRAPHY

Abbot, Charles Greeley. "The Relations between the Smithsonian Institution and the Wright Brothers," *Smithsonian Misc. Coll.*, LXXXI, 5 (1928). 27 pp.

—— "Samuel Pierpont Langley," *Smithsonian Misc. Coll.*, XCII, 8 (1934). 57 pp., 6 pls.

—— "The 1914 Tests of the Langley 'Aerodrome,'" *Smithsonian Misc. Coll.*, CIII, 8 (1942). 8 pp.

Adler, Cyrus. "Samuel Pierpont Langley," *Bull. Philosophical Soc. Washington*, XV (1907), 1-26.

—— *I Have Considered the Days*. Philadelphia: Jewish Publication Society of America, 1941. 447 pp., illus.

Bates, Ralph S. *Scientific Societies in the United States*. New York: John Wiley & Sons, 1945. 246 pp.

Dall, William Healey. *Spencer Fullerton Baird: A Biography*. Philadelphia and London: J. B. Lippincott, 1915. 462 pp., illus.

Darton, Nelson H. "Memorial of Charles Doolittle Walcott," *Bull. Geol. Soc. Amer.*, XXXIX (1928), 80-116, bibl. and portr.

Davis, W. M. "Biographical Memoir of John Wesley Powell, 1834-1902," *Nat. Acad. Sci. Biogr. Mem.*, VIII (1915), 11-83, portr.

Dickerson, Edward N. "Joseph Henry and the Magnetic Telegraph." An address delivered at Princeton College, June 16, 1885. New York: Scribner's, 1885. 65 pp.

Goode, George Brown. *Virginia Cousins: A Study of the Ancestry and Posterity of John Goode of Whitby, etc.* Richmond: J. W. Randolphe & English, 1887. 526 pp., illus. (Probably published in 1888, though the title page says

1887; G. B. G.'s dedication to his father, Francis Collier Goode, is dated May 1, 1888.)

Goode, George Brown. "Memories of Professor Baird," *The Chautauquan*, IX (1888), 21-24.

—— *The Smithsonian Institution, 1846-1896: The History of its First Half Century.* Published by the Institution, 1897. 856 pp., illus. (Chapters by S. P. Langley, G. B. Goode, Cyrus Adler, F. W. True, W. J. McGee, W. C. Winlock, Frank Baker, D. S. Jordan, T. C. Mendenhall, R. S. Woodward, E. S. Holden, Marcus Benjamin, W. N. Rice, E. D. Cope, W. G. Farlow, Theodore Gill, J. W. Fewkes, G. G. Hubbard, H. C. Bolton, D. C. Gilman, J. S. Billings, and A. R. Spofford.)
(See also under "Smithsonian Institution, 1901.")

James, James Alton. "The First Scientific Exploration of Russian America and the Purchase of Alaska," *Northwestern Univ. Studies in Social Sciences*, IV (1942). 276 pp.

Jordan, David Starr. *Leading American Men of Science.* New York: Henry Holt & Co., 1910. 471 pp.

Leffmann, Henry. "A Tribute: Samuel Pierpont Langley: Pioneer in Practical Aviation," *Journ. Franklin Inst.*, CLXXXVII, 1 (1919), 49-63.

Magie, W. F. "Joseph Henry," *Rev. Mod. Physics*, III, 4 (1931), 465-495.

Newcomb, Simon. "Biographical Memoir of Joseph Henry," *Nat. Acad. Sci. Biogr. Mem.*, V (1905), 1-45. (Published also in "A Memorial of Joseph Henry," U. S. Congress, 1880.)

Rathbun, Richard, "The National Gallery of Art," *U. S. Nat. Mus. Bull.* 70 (1909). 140 pp., illus.

—— "A Descriptive Account of the Building Recently Erected for the Departments of Natural History of the United States National Museum," *U. S. Nat. Mus. Bull.* 80 (1913). 131 pp., illus.

—— "The Columbian Institute for the Promotion of Arts and Sciences," *U. S. Nat. Mus. Bull.* 101 (1917). 85 pp.

[Rhees, William J.] *An Account of the Smithsonian Institution: Its Founding, Building, Operations, etc.* Philadelphia, 1866. 36 pp.

—— [editor]. "The Scientific Writings of James Smithson," *Smithsonian Misc. Coll.*, XXI (1879), 1-159. (See footnote, p. 7.)

Rhees, William J. "James Smithson and His Bequest," *Smithsonian Inst. Ann. Rep. for 1879* (1880), 143-210. (Published also, with illus., in *Smithsonian Misc. Coll.*, XXI [1879].)

—— [compiler and editor]. *The Smithsonian Institution: Documents Relating to its Origin and History, 1835-1899.* Published by the Institution, 1901. 2 vols., 1,857 pp.

Smith, George Otis. "Charles Doolittle Walcott," *Amer. Journ. Sci.*, Fifth Series, XIV, 1-6 (July, 1927). Also *Smithsonian Ann. Rep. 1927*, 555-561.)

Smithsonian Institution. *Annual Reports.* 1847-1947. (This unbroken series of reports, comprising one of the most remarkable achievements in American scientific publishing, is the prime source for any work on the history of the Smithsonian Institution.)

—— "A Memorial of George Brown Goode, together with a Selection of his Papers on Museums and on the History of Science in America," *Rep. U. S. Nat. Mus. for 1897*, Part 2 (1901). 515 pp., illus. (Eulogies by G. G. Hubbard, S. P. Langley, W. L. Wilson, H. F. Osborn, W. H. Dall; a "Memoir of George Brown Goode" by S. P. Langley; a bibliography of Goode's published writings, by R. I. Geare; and the following essays of Goode reprinted in full:

"Museum-History and Museums of History"
"The Genesis of the United States National Museum"
"The Principles of Museum Administration"
"The Museums of the Future"
"The Origin of the National Scientific and Educational Institutions of the United States"
"The Beginnings of Natural History in America"
"The Beginnings of American Science"
"The First National Science Congress (Washington, April 1844) and Its Connection with the Organization of the American Association"

—— "Samuel Pierpont Langley Memorial Meeting, December 3, 1906: Addresses by A. D. White, W. H. Pickering, and Octave Chanute," *Smithsonian Misc. Coll.*, XLIX, 4 (1907). 48 pp.

Taylor, William B. "A Memoir of Joseph Henry: A Sketch of his Scientific Work," *Bull. Philos. Soc. Washington*, II (1878), 230-368. (Includes list of Henry's scientific papers.)

Taylor, William B. "Henry and the Telegraph," *Ann. Rep. Smithsonian Inst. for 1878* (1879), 263-360.

Terres, John K. "Smithsonian 'Bird Man': A Biographical Sketch of Alexander Wetmore." *Audubon Mag.*, L (May-June, 1948), 160-167, illus.

True, Webster P. *The First Hundred Years of the Smithsonian Institution*. Published by the Institution for the Smithsonian Centennial, 1946. 64 pp., illus.

United States Congress. *A Memorial of Joseph Henry, 1880.* 508 pp. (Addresses by Asa Gray, James A. Garfield, William T. Sherman, et al., and biographical memoir by Simon Newcomb; published also in *Smithsonian Misc. Coll.*, XXI [1879].)

Walcott, Charles Doolittle. "Biographical Memoir of Samuel Pierpont Langley, 1834-1906," *Nat. Acad. Sci. Biogr. Mem.*, VII (1912), 245-68.

—— "Samuel Pierpont Langley and Modern Aviation," *Proc. Amer. Philos. Soc.*, LXV (1926), 79-82.

Welling, James C. "Life and Character of Joseph Henry," *Bull. Philos. Soc. Washington*, II (1878), 203-229.

INDEX

209

WHO CAN SAY WHAT THE COND IONS OF science in the United States would be today but for the Smithsonian Institution, made possible by the amazing bequest of the bachelor English chemist, James Smithson.

No stranger story exists in the annals of human culture than the origin of the "Smithsonian." No one has been able to explain Smithson's motive in drawing up a will which resulted in the delivery, in September, 1838, of £104,960 in gold sovereigns from the clipper ship *Mediator* to the Philadelphia mint, where it was recoined into American money, $508,-318.46.

The odd Smithson had once said, "The man of science is of no country, the world is his country, all mankind his countrymen." In this luminous statement lies partially, perhaps, the explanation for his now famous will that, should his sole relative, nephew Henry James Hungerford, die without issue, the whole estate should go—

to the United States of America to found at Washington under the name of Smithsonian Institution, an establishment for the increase and diffusion of knowledge among men.

Mr. Oehser here relates for the general reader the life-story of the Smithsonian through the six or eight great figures who have steered its course and have made it one of the world's leading cultural and scientific centers. Here are colorful biographies of Joseph Henry, the great physicist; Spencer Fullerton Baird, biologist; George Brown Goode, museum expert; Samuel Pierpont Langley, world-known astronomer and pioneer in "flying machines"; Charles Walcott, geologist; Charles Greeley Abbot, physicist and astronomer; Alexander Wetmore, ornithologist and Smithsonian Secretary since 1945.

This book provides the answer to the question of people who all their lives have known the name "Smithsonian"—"Just what *is* the Smithsonian Institution?" It orients the reader or the visitor to Washington who knows Smithsonian as one of the nation's landmarks. He is led to an old red-stone, cathedral-like building which is called the Smithsonian; he visits the magnificent National Gallery of Art nearby and the Freer Art Gallery, and is told that these, also, are a part of the Smithsonian; he goes out to the Zoo in Rock Creek Park and learns that this National Zoological Park, too, is under Smithsonian direction. And he discovers to his further surprise that seven or eight additional important "bureaus" fall within the Smithsonian family.

Thus, SONS OF SCIENCE conducts the reader through more than a hundred fascinating years of the Smithsonian's life-story. Here you will learn, unforgettably, how the Smithsonian has become America's scientific nerve-center, enjoying the advantages of a privately endowed in-